# INSPIRE MATHS

# TEACHER'S GUIDE 1A

**Consultant and author**
Dr Fong Ho Kheong

**Authors**
Chelvi Ramakrishnan and Bernice Lau Pui Wah

**UK consultants**
Carole Skinner, Simon d'Angelo and Elizabeth Gibbs

**OXFORD**
UNIVERSITY PRESS

© 2015 Marshall Cavendish Education Pte Ltd

**Published by Marshall Cavendish Education**
Times Centre, 1 New Industrial Road, Singapore 536196
Customer Service Hotline: (65) 6213 9444
Email: tmesales@mceducation.com
Website: www.mceducation.com

Distributed by
**Oxford University Press**
Great Clarendon Street, Oxford,
OX2 6DP, United Kingdom
www.oxfordprimary.co.uk
www.oxfordowl.co.uk

First published 2015
Reprinted 2015, 2016 (twice), 2017

ISBN 978-981-01-8866-5

Printed in the United Kingdom

Acknowledgements
Written by Dr Fong Ho Kheong, Chelvi Ramakrishnan and Bernice Lau Pui Wah

UK consultants: Carole Skinner, Simon d'Angelo and Elizabeth Gibbs

Cover artwork by Daron Parton

The authors and publisher would like to thank all schools and individuals who helped to trial and review Inspire Maths resources.

# Contents

# The background to *Inspire Maths*

### A letter from Dr Fong Ho Kheong

Dear Colleague,

I am both humbled and proud to see that my work has now been adapted for use in many countries. *My Pals are Here!*, the series from which *Inspire Maths* is adapted, has been translated into languages including Spanish, Indonesian, Dutch and Arabic, and the books are used by millions of children all over the world.

International surveys show that children taught with the series score higher than their peers in standardised tests, and also that it helps young children to become more confident with maths. The 2012 PISA survey again placed Singapore's children at the top of international rankings for mathematics; the country also had the highest percentage of top achievers. In the USA, it was reported in 2013 that schools in the Fayette County, West Virginia who had adopted the programme had made impressive progress in their mathematics results, including a 12 per cent improvement among third graders in one school and a 20 per cent improvement among fourth graders in another.

**Why does *Inspire Maths* work?** A major strength of *Inspire Maths* is its robust structure, based on best-practice principles and methods of teaching and learning mathematics, including the concrete-pictorial-abstract (CPA) and scaffolding approaches, and a systematic teaching pathway. This comprehensive pathway emphasises mastery – with continuous, active reinforcement of concepts to help children assimilate and accommodate their learning – followed by extension, challenging children to develop and practise the thinking skills that will enable them to become confident, critically aware and independent learners. The textbooks from which *Inspire Maths* is adapted have also been informed by continuous evaluation of their success in the classroom, through a process of school visits, classroom observation and programme review. Because of this, *Inspire Maths* gives you a proven framework for supporting children of all abilities to achieve success.

*Inspire Maths* is based on well-established constructivist ideas of learning, and the views of internationally-renowned educationalists including Jerome Bruner, Jean Piaget, Lev Vygotsky, Richard Skemp and David Ausubel. Constructivism underpins the programme's approach to learning mathematical concepts and skills through assimilation and accommodation, and their reinforcement through reflective activities such as journal writing and error correction. This perspective is also reflected in the programme's emphasis on mastery learning and building children's confidence.

More particularly, Bruner's three modes of representation are mirrored by the concrete–pictorial–abstract learning progression which is central to *Inspire Maths*. Bruner's ideas parallel Piaget's stages of development; essentially, children's understanding of mathematical concepts depends on their stage of development. Learning in the early stages is achieved through concrete representation. Then, when ready, children can move on to pictorial representations – such as the bar model – which in turn provide them with a bridge to the abstract stage, and a flexible, fully independent understanding of the abstract, symbolic language of maths. Though it cannot be used to tackle every problem, the bar model has a particularly significant role in helping children at the concrete and semi-concrete operational stage (Piaget's developmental theory) to approach and solve problems successfully.

Skemp's ideas about instrumental and relational understanding are also an important part of the pedagogy underpinning *Inspire Maths*. Skemp suggests that learning mathematics by relating ideas to each other (relational understanding) is more meaningful, and therefore more effective, than memorising facts and procedures (instrumental understanding). Building on these ideas, *Inspire Maths* is designed to develop children's lasting and profound mathematical understanding which they will continue to extend and apply.

I would like to congratulate the UK schools and teachers who have made the choice to use *Inspire Maths*. I am confident that your children will experience similar success to that seen in other countries who have adopted this approach.

Dr Fong

Dr Fong achieved a PhD in Mathematics Education from King's College London before teaching mathematics in the National Institute of Education, Nanyang Technological University, for over 24 years. He is currently a senior Mathematics Specialist with the Regional Centre for Education in Science and Mathematics (RECSAM) in Penang, Malaysia. He has published more than 100 journal articles, research reports, and primary and secondary mathematics books, and his research work includes diagnosing children with mathematical difficulties and teaching thinking skills to solve mathematical problems.

# What is *Inspire Maths?*

*Inspire Maths* is the UK edition of *My Pals are Here!*, the internationally renowned approach used to teach maths in Singapore, which was heavily influenced by the Cockroft report of 1982[1]. Singapore's Ministry of Education drew on leading international research on effective teaching and learning of mathematics to meet the challenge of raising primary mathematics attainment within Singapore's schools.

The approach to mathematics teaching and learning that was developed was further refined over subsequent decades and it is this approach that is central to *My Pals are Here!* Authored by Dr Fong Ho Kheong and first published in 2001, *My Pals are Here!* is used by almost 100% of State Primary schools and over 80% of Primary schools in Singapore.

Dr Fong's overarching aim in developing *My Pals are Here!* was to help all children understand and use mathematics confidently and competently, and to support non-specialist maths teachers to deliver this. The programme's success in achieving this aim is reflected in the high levels of mathematics attainment by Singapore's pupils, who are consistently ranked among the very top in international comparison studies such as PISA and TIMSS. It is also reflected in the results of schools outside Singapore that have adopted the series, for example, in the USA and South Africa.

*Inspire Maths* provides a highly scaffolded learning framework with problem solving at its heart. It is built on a focused, coherent and cumulative spiral curriculum that continuously builds and consolidates knowledge to reach deep understanding. The programme encourages extensive practice to develop fluency and mastery, so that every child – across all abilities – can succeed at mathematics.

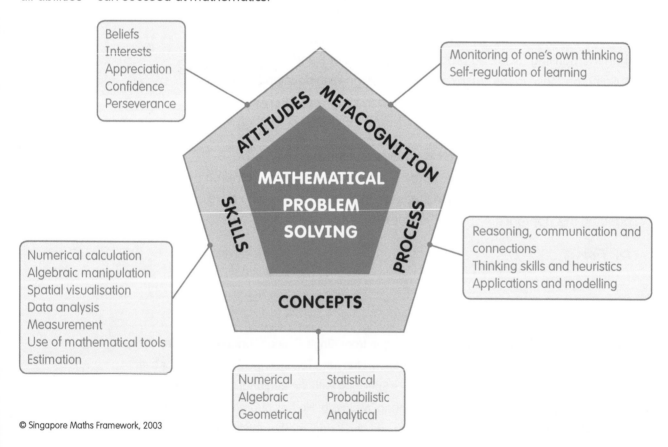

© Singapore Maths Framework, 2003

**The principles that underpin *Inspire Maths***

---

1   Mathematics Counts, Dr W.H.Cockroft, 1982

# The concrete-pictorial-abstract approach

*Inspire Maths* emphasises the development of critical thinking and problem solving skills, which help children make connections to develop deeper understanding. The powerful concrete–pictorial–abstract (CPA) approach, including the bar model method, is central to this.

Why is the CPA approach so powerful? From very early on in their school life, we expect children to use and understand numbers, which are abstract concepts. Many children struggle with this and so their first experiences of mathematics can be confusing, leaving them with no solid foundation to build on for later learning. The CPA approach helps children achieve secure number sense – that is, a sense of what numbers really represent and how to use them mathematically. This is done through a series of carefully structured representations – first using physical objects (concrete), then diagrams or pictures (pictorial), and ultimately using representations such as numerals (abstract).

In the example below from *Inspire Maths* Pupil Textbook 1A, children are exploring order and pattern. Using the CPA approach, they explore with interlocking cubes, then using a number track, and finally through words, written symbols and calculations.

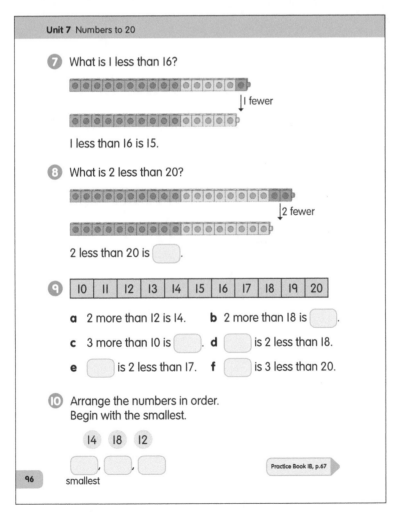

*Inspire Maths* **Pupil Textbook 1A, page 96**

# The bar model

The bar model is a step-by-step method that helps children to understand and extract the information within a calculation or word problem. By drawing a bar model, children translate a calculation or word problem into a picture. The approach helps children process the information given in the problem, visualise the structure, make connections and solve the problem.

The bar model is first introduced in *Inspire Maths* 2. In the following activity, children explore addition and subtraction initially with concrete apparatus before moving on to using a pictorial representation – the bar model.

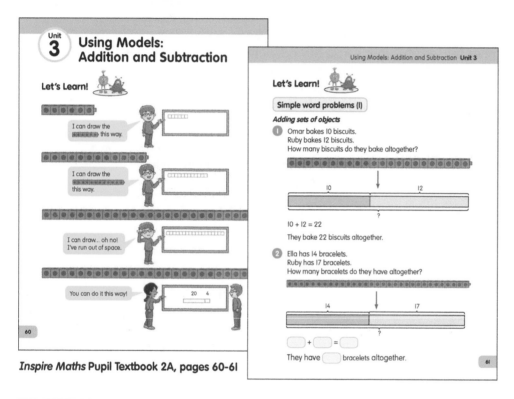

*Inspire Maths* Pupil Textbook 2A, pages 60-61

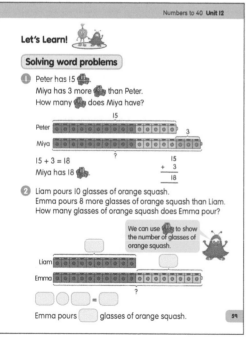

*Inspire Maths* Pupil Textbook 1B, page 59

In *Inspire Maths* 1, children are prepared for the introduction of the bar model by using concrete apparatus; for example, using interlocking cubes to compare the number of objects in two groups.

# Heuristics for problem solving

*Inspire Maths* helps children learn to use *heuristics* to solve problems. *Heuristics* refers to the different strategies that children can adopt to solve unfamiliar or non-routine problems. These strategies include drawing the bar model, pattern-spotting, using diagrams and estimating or 'guess and check'.

In this example from *Inspire Maths* Pupil Textbook IA, children spot patterns and relationships to solve the problems.

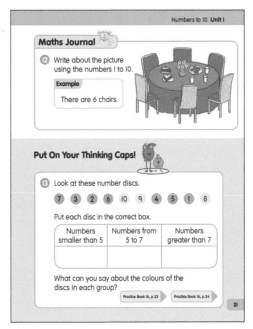

*Inspire Maths* Pupil Textbook IA, page 21

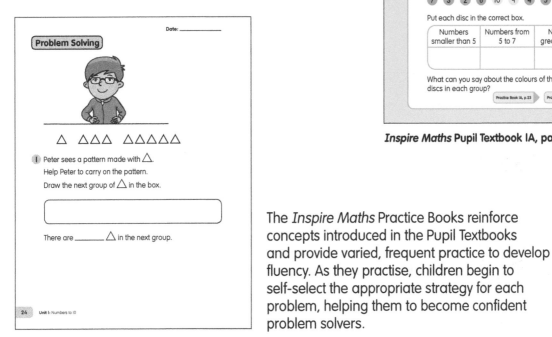

*Inspire Maths* Practice Book IA, page 24

The *Inspire Maths* Practice Books reinforce concepts introduced in the Pupil Textbooks and provide varied, frequent practice to develop fluency. As they practise, children begin to self-select the appropriate strategy for each problem, helping them to become confident problem solvers.

## Higher-order questioning

*Inspire Maths* is designed to stimulate thinking beyond the activities from the Pupil Textbooks. The activities should kick-start mathematically meaningful conversations through questioning, giving children opportunities to think mathematically, discover connections and be creative.

You can use written problems as a starting point for further questioning, for example, when presented with 7 + 4 = II and an accompanying bar model, you might ask, 'What would happen if it was II – 4? Or II – 7? What about 7 + 4 or 4 + 7?' Then take it further: 'What would the bar model look like if it was 8 + 4?'

Modelling higher-order questioning at every opportunity will encourage children to use this strategy to explore and solve problems for themselves.

# Making use of variation

Research shows that mathematical and perceptual variation deepens understanding as it constantly challenges children to develop their existing understanding by looking at questions from different perspectives and adapting to new situations. The numbers and problems in *Inspire Maths* activities have been specifically selected on this basis to challenge children as the questions progress and lead them towards mastery.

## Mathematical variation

With mathematical variation, the mathematical concept, for example addition, stays the same but the mathematics (and what children physically 'do') varies. For example, children may look at addition *without* regrouping or *with* regrouping. The variation challenges children to use their mathematical skills flexibly to suit the situation, deepening understanding.

## Perceptual variation

With perceptual variation, the mathematical concept is the same throughout the sequence of questions but is presented in different ways. This activity from *Inspire Maths* Pupil Textbook IA presents different ways of perceiving number bonds and encourages children to look for connections between the questions. For example, between questions I and 2, the total number of beads increases by two, and the number of beads visible under one cup increases by one, so the number of beads hidden under the second cup will increase by one.

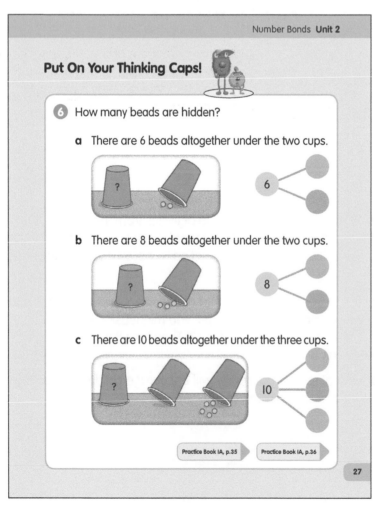

*Inspire Maths* Pupil Textbook IA, page 27

# The *Inspire Maths* teaching pathway

*Inspire Maths* is a programme that teaches to mastery. It is built on a cumulative spiral curriculum, focusing on core topics to build deep understanding. The *Inspire Maths* teaching pathway scaffolds in-depth learning of key mathematical concepts through the development of problem-solving and critical thinking skills, and extensive opportunities for practice.

## Pupil Textbooks to scaffold new learning

*Inspire Maths* Pupil Textbooks present new learning clearly and consistently, providing a highly scaffolded framework to support all children. Mathematical concepts are presented visually, with specific and structured activities, to build firm foundations. There are two Pupil Textbooks for each level.

### *Let's Learn!* to build firm foundations

Carefully scaffolded learning through *Let's Learn!* activities in the *Inspire Maths* Pupil Textbooks promotes deep mathematical understanding through:

- clearly presented pages to illustrate how the CPA approach can be used to build firm foundations

- careful questioning to support the use of concrete apparatus

- opportunities for higher-order questioning (see page ix) to help children become confident and competent problem solvers

- opportunities to assess each child's understanding and prior knowledge through observing their use of concrete apparatus and how they approach the activity

- use of mathematical talk to explore and develop reasoning skills.

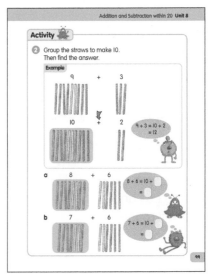

*Inspire Maths* Pupil Textbook 1A, page 98

### Guided practice to develop deep understanding

After a concept has been introduced in *Let's Learn!*, guided practice develops the deep understanding required for mastery. Support and guide children as they work collaboratively in pairs or small groups through the guided practice activities indicated by empty coloured boxes in the Pupil Textbook.

Frequent opportunities for guided practice:

- help children develop deep understanding

- develop mathematical language and reasoning through collaborative work

- provide further opportunities to check children's understanding by observing their use of concrete apparatus and listening to their discussions

- help you to provide appropriate intervention – guiding those who need extra support and challenging those who are ready for the next step.

*Inspire Maths* Pupil Textbook 1A, page 99

## Let's Explore! and Games to investigate and apply learning

Engaging games and investigative *Let's Explore!* activities in the *Inspire Maths* Pupil Textbooks encourage children to apply concepts they have been learning and provide an opportunity to assess their reasoning skills by observing how they approach the tasks.

Children work collaboratively in small groups or pairs:

- games reinforce skills, concepts and problem solving strategies leading to mastery

- *Let's Explore!* activities encourage children to investigate connections through mathematical reasoning

- meaningful discussion and conversation develop mathematical language.

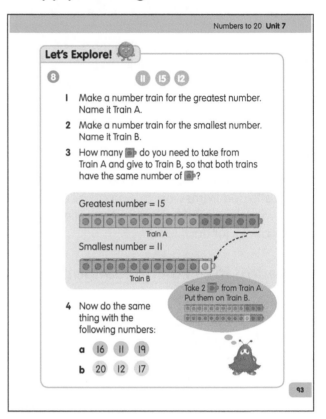

Inspire Maths Pupil Textbook IA, Page 93

## Maths Journal to reflect

The *Maths Journal* is where each child records their mathematical thinking and reflects on their learning. The typical Maths Journal would be a child's own exercise book or notebook – something that the child 'owns', can share with you, with parents or carers, and that builds up over time.

Children reflect on their learning through their Maths Journal:

- giving both the child and you a valuable assessment tool, showing progress over time

- providing opportunities for children to discuss their thinking with each other, parents or carers, and with you, helping to establish next steps and giving a sense of pride in their achievements.

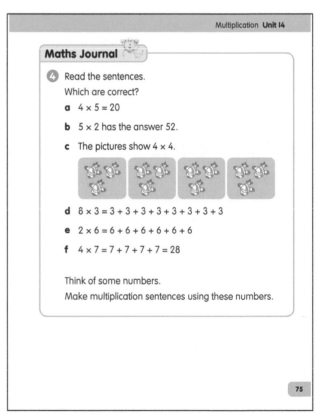

Inspire Maths Pupil Textbook IB, Page 75

## *Put on Your Thinking Caps!* to challenge

Each unit concludes with a *Put on Your Thinking Caps!* activity in the Pupil Textbook which challenges children to solve non-routine problems.

Challenging activities:

- ask children to draw on prior knowledge as well as newly learned concepts

- ask children to use problem solving strategies and critical thinking skills, for example sequencing or comparing

- provide valuable opportunities to assess whether children have developed a deep understanding of a concept by listening to their explanations of their mathematical thinking and looking at how they model the problem, for example using concrete apparatus and pictorial representations.

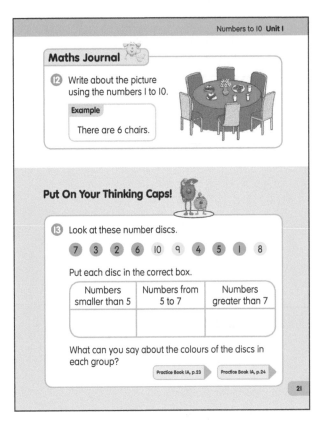

*Inspire Maths* Pupil Textbook 1A, page 21

## *Home Maths* to encourage mathematical conversations

Home maths activities in the Pupil Textbooks are engaging, hands-on suggestions that parents and carers can use with children to explore maths further outside the classroom, for example through finding shapes in pictures and around the house.

Engaging home activities:

- help you to involve parents and carers in their child's mathematical learning

- help children to see maths in the world around them.

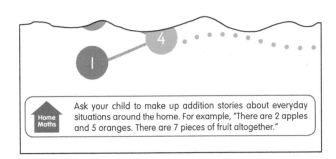

*Inspire Maths* Pupil Textbook 1A, page 35

## Practice Books to develop fluency and consolidate

*Inspire Maths* Practice Books provide carefully structured questions to reinforce concepts introduced in the Pupil Textbooks and to provide varied, frequent practice. A wealth of activities develop fluency, build mathematical confidence and lead towards mastery. The Practice Books are also a valuable record of individual progress. There are four Practice Books for *Inspire Maths* 1-3 and two Practice Books for *Inspire Maths* 4-6.

Each Practice Book includes:

- **Challenging Practice** and **Problem Solving** activities to develop children's critical thinking skills

- **Reviews** after every two or three units, to reinforce learning

- **Revisions** that draw from a range of preceding topics, concepts and strands, for more complete consolidation.

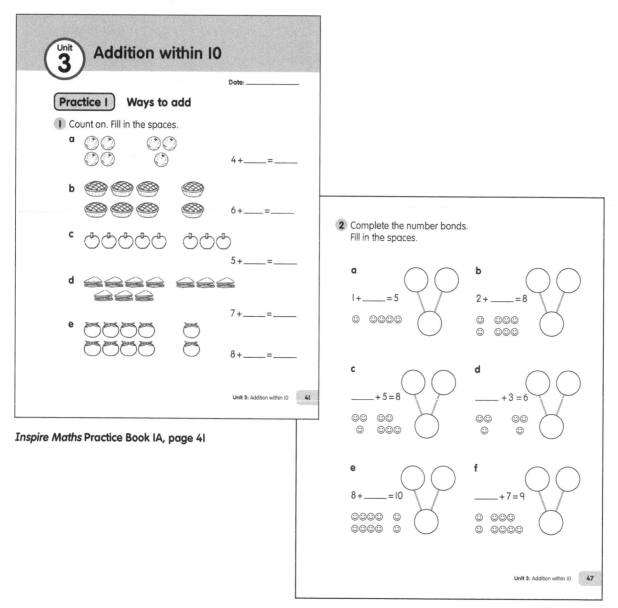

*Inspire Maths* **Practice Book IA, page 41**

*Inspire Maths* **Practice Book IA, page 47**

## Assessment Books to create a record of progress

*Inspire Maths* provides comprehensive Assessment Books with regular summative assessments to create a record of progress for each child, as well as giving children opportunities to reflect on their own learning. The wraparound assessment provided through the *Inspire Maths* teaching pathway in combination with the *Inspire Maths* Assessment Books enables rapid, appropriate intervention as soon as a child needs it, before they fall behind and when they are ready to be challenged. Topics and concepts are frequently revisited in the assessments, helping to build mastery.

There is one Assessment Book for each level, providing complete coverage of the key concepts across a year. Each assessment is divided into sections so you can easily break them down into appropriate chunks to suit your class. For the early levels, you may choose to assess in small groups, reading out the questions and scribing answers. Encourage children to use concrete apparatus when they need support to help them work through the questions.

There are three types of assessment within each Assessment Book:

1. **Main assessments:** The main assessments cover the key learning objectives from the preceding two or three units of the Pupil Textbooks. Through the main assessments, children are given opportunities to apply their learning in a variety of different contexts, helping you to quickly identify which children are ready to move on and which need further support. Children may self-mark to reflect on their progress.

2. **Check-ups:** There are four check-ups for each level which revisit the previous units, drawing on prior knowledge to encourage children to make connections and apply their learning to solve problems. These assessments give you valuable opportunities to check children's understanding through observing how they approach questions, use and interpret mathematical language and use heuristics.

3. **Challenging Problems:** These assessments make use of non-routine and unfamiliar questions to see how children use their repertoire of strategies to tackle more challenging problems. Use this as an opportunity to assess children's mathematical thinking, reasoning and problem solving skills by looking at their methods and how they approach the problem. They are particularly suitable for extension and assessing a child's level of mastery.

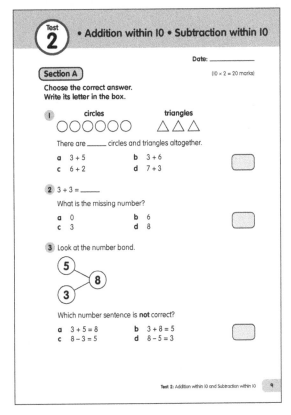

*Inspire Maths* Assessment Book 1, page 9

# Using the Teacher's Guide

There are two *Inspire Maths* Teacher's Guides for each level, one per Pupil Textbook. Each Teacher's Guide contains:

- information on how to get started
- long-term planning support
- medium-term planning support
- suggested teaching sequence for each pupil textbook page
- answers
- photocopiable activities.

**Key concepts** clearly outline the important ideas children will be introduced to within each unit.

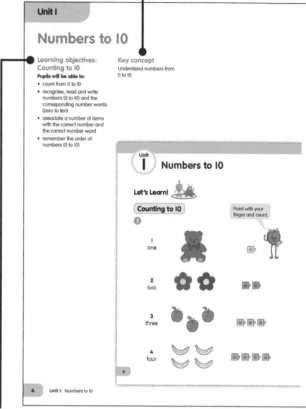

*Inspire Maths* Teacher's Guide IA, pages 4-5

**Learning objectives** clearly signal the aims of the unit, which are designed to help children develop their understanding of the unit's key concepts. Children are introduced to the learning objectives in the Pupil Textbook. The Practice Book provides opportunities to practise and consolidate for mastery.

Ideas for **further practice activities** to develop fluency are outlined in every unit.

The **teaching sequence** provides clear step-by-step guidance towards meeting the learning objectives. It highlights problem solving strategies to focus on and support for meaningful mathematical conversation and making the best use of concrete apparatus.

Links to the Practice Books provide opportunities for **independent work** when children are ready, to develop fluency and lead towards mastery.

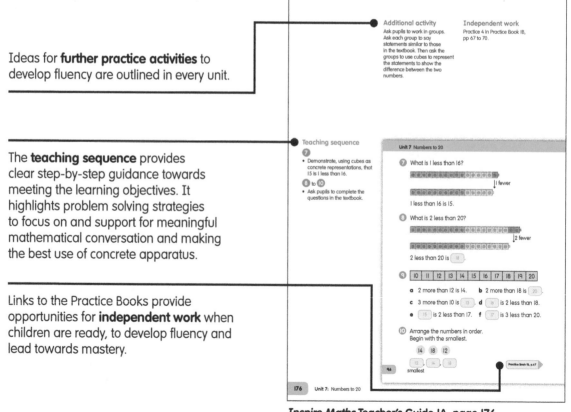

*Inspire Maths* Teacher's Guide IA, page 176

**Equipment** needed for each Pupil Textbook page is listed to help you prepare for the activities.

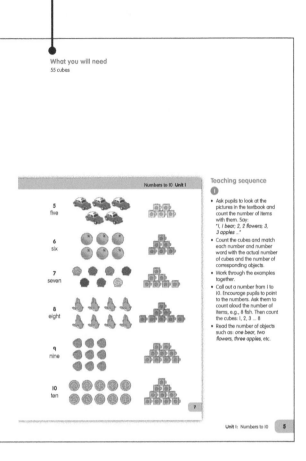

What you will need
55 cubes

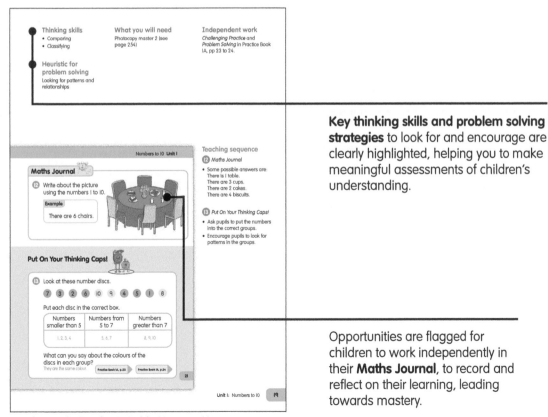

**Key thinking skills and problem solving strategies** to look for and encourage are clearly highlighted, helping you to make meaningful assessments of children's understanding.

Opportunities are flagged for children to work independently in their **Maths Journal**, to record and reflect on their learning, leading towards mastery.

*Inspire Maths* Teacher's Guide IA, page 19

# Long-term planning

| Unit title | Key concepts |
|---|---|
| **1 Numbers to 10** | |
| Counting to 10 | • Understand numbers from 0 to 10 |
| Compare | • Two sets of objects can be compared using the method of one-to-one correspondence<br>• The number of objects can be the same as, smaller than or greater than another set of objects |
| Order and pattern | • A sequence of objects and numbers can form a pattern |
| **2 Number Bonds** | |
| Making number bonds | • Adding two or more numbers gives another number |
| **Practice Book – Review 1** | |
| **Assessment Book – Test 1** | |
| **3 Addition within 10** | |
| Ways to add | • Adding is associated with the 'part-whole' and 'adding on' concepts |
| Making up addition stories | |
| Solving word problems | • Applying the 'part-whole' and 'adding on' concepts in addition |
| **4 Subtraction within 10** | |
| Ways to subtract | • Subtracting is associated with the 'part-whole' and 'taking away' concepts |
| Making up subtraction stories | |
| Solving word problems | • Applying the 'part-whole' and 'taking away' concepts in subtraction |
| Making a family of number sentences | • A family of number sentences can be written from a set of three related numbers |
| **Practice Book – Review 2** | |
| **Assessment Book – Test 2, Challenging Problems 1, Check-up 1** | |
| **5 Shapes and Patterns** | |
| Getting to know shapes | • A circle has no corners and no sides<br>• A square has 4 equal sides and 4 corners<br>• A triangle has 3 sides and 3 corners<br>• A rectangle has 4 sides (opposite sides are equal) and 4 corners |
| Making pictures from shapes | • Shapes such as circles, triangles, squares and rectangles can be used to make pictures |
| Seeing shapes in things around us | • When an object is viewed from different angles/sides, we can see different shapes. For example, the top view of a tin of soup is a circle |
| Getting to know patterns | • Patterns are formed by repeating a particular arrangement of shape, size and/or colour placed next to each other |
| Making more patterns | • Patterns can be formed by repeating a particular arrangement of objects placed next to each other |

| Unit title | Key concepts |
|---|---|
| **6 Ordinal numbers** | |
| Knowing ordinal numbers | • Ordinal numbers are for describing the position of something |
| Naming left and right positions | • Positions from the left and right can be named using ordinal numbers |
| **Practice Book – Review 3** | |
| **7 Numbers to 20** | |
| Counting to 20 | • Use one-to-one correspondence in counting |
| Place value | • Numbers to 20 can be represented as tens and ones in a place value chart |
| Compare | • Numbers to 20 can be compared using the terms 'greater than' and 'smaller than' as well as by arranging in ascending or descending order |
| Order and pattern | • Numbers can be arranged in order and made into a pattern |
| **Assessment Book – Test 3** | |
| **8 Addition and Subtraction within 20** | |
| Ways to add | • Two I-digit numbers can be added by using the 'make 10' strategy and the 'regrouping into tens and ones' strategy |
| Ways to subtract | • 2-digit numbers can be regrouped into tens and ones |
| Solving word problems | • Applying the 'part-whole', 'adding on' and 'taking away' concepts in addition and subtraction |
| **9 Length** | |
| Comparing two things | • The lengths of two objects can be compared using the terms 'tall/taller', 'long/longer', 'short/shorter' and 'high/higher' |
| Comparing more things | • The lengths of more than two objects can be compared using the terms 'tallest', 'longest', 'shortest' and 'highest' |
| Using a start line | • A common starting point makes comparison of lengths easier |
| Measuring things | • Length can be measured using objects as non-standard units |
| Finding lengths in units | • Length can be described using the term 'unit' instead of paper clips or lolly sticks |
| **Practice Book – Revision I** | |
| **Assessment Book – Test 4, Challenging Problems 2, Check-up 2** | |
| **10 Mass** | |
| Comparing things | • Compare masses using a pan balance |
| Finding the masses of things | • Mass can be measured using objects as non-standard units |
| Finding mass in units | • Mass can be described using the term 'units' |
| **11 Picture graphs** | |
| Simple picture graphs | • Data can be collected and organised into a horizontal or vertical picture graph for interpretation |
| More picture graphs | • Data can be collected and organised into a horizontal or vertical picture graph using symbols |
| **Assessment Book – Test 5** | |

| Unit title | Key concepts |
|---|---|
| **12 Numbers to 40** | |
| Counting to 40 | • Using one-to-one correspondence in counting<br>• I ten equals ten ones |
| Place value | • Numbers to 40 can be represented as tens and ones in a place value chart |
| Comparing, order and pattern | • Numbers to 40 can be compared using the terms 'greater than' / 'smaller than' and 'greatest' / 'smallest' as well as arranged in ascending or descending order |
| Simple addition | • 'Add on' and 'part-whole' concepts are used in adding numbers |
| More addition | • 'Add on' and 'part-whole' concepts are used in adding numbers<br>• Regrouping concept can be applied in addition |
| Simple subtraction | • The 'taking away' concept is used in subtraction |
| More subtraction | |
| Adding three numbers | • 'Add on' and 'making ten' concepts are used in adding three numbers<br>• The regrouping concept is also applied |
| Solving word problems | • The 'part-whole', 'taking away', 'adding on' and 'comparing' concepts are used to solve word problems involving addition and subtraction |
| **Practice Book – Review 4** | |
| **13 Mental calculations** | |
| Mental addition | • A 2-digit number can be conceptualised as tens and ones<br>• Adding is conceptualised as adding or putting parts together |
| Mental subtraction | • A 2-digit number can be conceptualised as tens and ones<br>• Subtracting is conceptualised as taking away from a whole |
| **14 Multiplication** | |
| Adding the same number | • Multiplication is conceptualised as repeated addition |
| Making multiplication stories | • Tell stories based on the multiplication concept and repeated addition |
| Solving word problems | • Applying the multiplication concept to solve word problems |
| **Practice Book – Review 5** | |
| **Assessment Book – Test 6, Challenging Problems 3, Check-up 3** | |
| **15  Division** | |
| Sharing equally | • Division is conceptualised as dividing a set of objects equally |
| Finding the numbers of groups | • Division is conceptualised as sharing a set of items equally into groups |
| **16 Time** | |
| Telling the time to the hour | • Time can be used to measure the duration of an event |
| Telling the time to the half hour | • Measuring half an hour using the term 'half past' |
| **Practice Book – Review 6** | |
| **Assessment Book – Test 7** | |

| Unit title | Key concepts |
|---|---|
| **17 Numbers to 100** | |
| Counting | • Using one-to-one correspondence in counting<br>• 1 ten is the same as 10 ones<br>• 10 tens is 100 |
| Place value | • Numbers to 100 can be represented as tens and ones in a place value chart |
| Comparing, order and pattern | • Numbers to 100 can be compared using the terms 'greater than' and 'smaller than'<br>• Numbers to 100 can be arranged in ascending or descending order |
| Simple addition | • The 'adding on' and 'part-whole' concepts are used in adding numbers |
| More addition | • The 'adding on' and 'part-whole' concepts are used in adding numbers<br>• The regrouping concept is applied in addition |
| Simple subtraction | • The 'taking away' concept is used in subtraction |
| More subtraction | |
| **18 Money (1)** | |
| Getting to know our money | • Coins and notes in pounds and pence can be used to pay for goods and services. |
| Exchanging money | • A coin or note of one denomination can be used as the equivalent of another set of coins or notes of a smaller denomination |
| Work out the amount of money | • The amount of money can be counted in pence (up to £1) and pounds (up to £100) |
| **19 Money (2)** | |
| Adding and subtracting in pence | • Addition and subtraction concepts in numbers are used in addition and subtraction of money |
| Adding and subtracting in pounds | |
| Solving word problems | • The 'part-whole', 'adding on', 'taking away' and 'comparing' concepts in addition and subtraction are used in solving word problems |
| **Practice Book – Revision 2** | |
| **Assessment Book – Test 8, Challenging Problems 4, Check-up 4** | |

# Medium-term plan

| Week | Learning Objectives | Thinking Skills | Resources |
|---|---|---|---|
| I | **(I) Counting to I0**<br><br>Pupils will be able to:<br>• count from 0 to I0<br>• recognise, read and write numbers (0 to I0) and the corresponding number words (zero to ten)<br>• associate a number of items with the correct number and the correct number word<br>• remember the order of numbers (0 to I0) | | • Pupil Textbook IA, pp 6 to I2<br>• Practice Book IA, pp 5 to I2<br>• Teacher's Guide IA, pp 4 to I0 |
| I | **(2) Compare**<br><br>Pupils will be able to:<br>• compare two sets of objects (using the method of one-to-one correspondence) and identify the set that has more, fewer or the same number of objects<br>• use the terms 'more than' and 'fewer than' when comparing two sets of objects<br>• compare two numbers using the terms 'greater than' or 'smaller than' | • Comparing | • Pupil Textbook IA, pp I3 to I6<br>• Practice Book IA, pp I3 to I8<br>• Teacher's Guide IA, pp II to I4 |

# Unit I: Numbers to I0

| Week | Learning Objectives | Thinking Skills | Resources |
|---|---|---|---|
| 2 | **(3) Order and pattern**<br><br>Pupils will be able to:<br>• compare the number of items from a sequence of objects and find the number of objects in a sequence<br>• interpret and use statements containing 'I more than' or 'I less than' a given number | • Comparing<br>• Sequencing | • Pupil Textbook IA, pp I7 to 2I<br>• Practice Book IA, pp I9 to 22<br>• Teacher's Guide IA, pp I5 to I9 |
| 2 | *Put On Your Thinking Caps!* | • Comparing<br>• Classifying<br><br>Heuristic for problem solving:<br>• Looking for patterns and relationships | • Pupil Textbook IA, p 2I<br>• Practice Book IA, pp 23 to 24<br>• Teacher's Guide IA, p I9 |

# Numbers to 10

## Learning objectives:
## Counting to 10

**Pupils will be able to:**

- count from 0 to 10
- recognise, read and write numbers (0 to 10) and the corresponding number words (zero to ten)
- associate a number of items with the correct number and the correct number word
- remember the order of numbers (0 to 10)

## Key concept

Understand numbers from 0 to 10

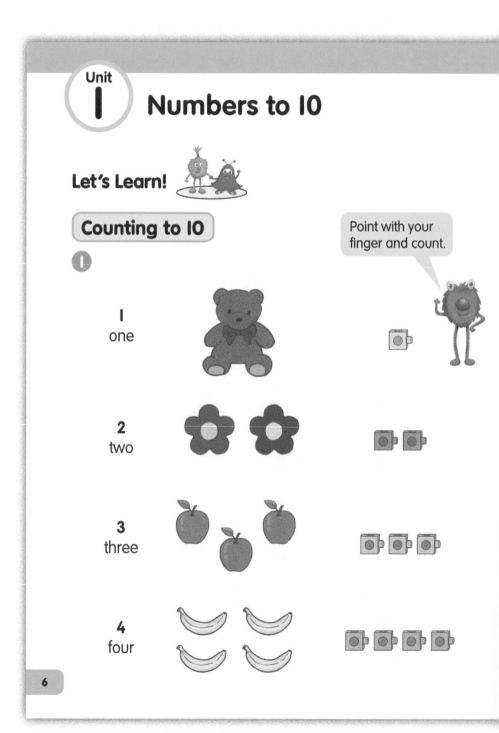

## What you will need
55 cubes

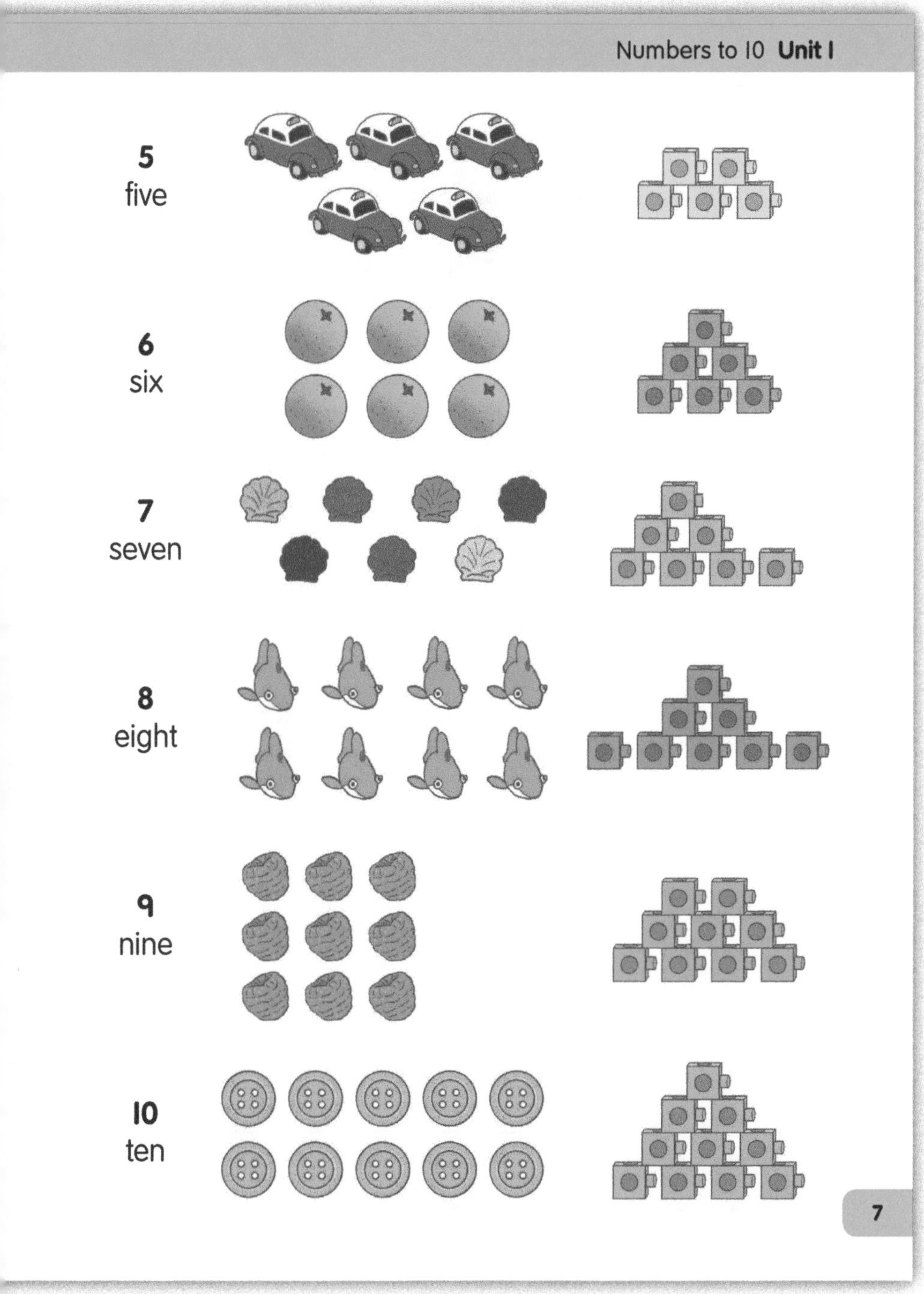

5
five

6
six

7
seven

8
eight

9
nine

I0
ten

7

## Teaching sequence

I

- Ask pupils to look at the pictures in the textbook and count the number of items with them. Say:
"I, I bear; 2, 2 flowers; 3, 3 apples ..."
- Count the cubes and match each number and number word with the actual number of cubes and the number of corresponding objects.
- Work through the examples together.
- Call out a number from I to I0. Encourage pupils to point to the numbers. Ask them to count aloud the number of items, e.g., 8 fish. Then count the cubes: I, 2, 3 ... 8
- Read the number of objects such as: *one bear, two flowers, three apples,* etc.

## What you will need
10 cubes

## Teaching sequence

- Hold 10 cubes in your hand. Ask pupils to count the number of cubes aloud.
- Remove one cube and ask pupils to count the remaining cubes. Repeat this until there are no cubes left.
- Introduce the concept of '0' and the number word 'zero'.
- Invite a volunteer to hold 5 cubes. Say:

  *"You have 5 cubes. Take away I cube. How many cubes do you have left?"*

- Remove the cubes one at a time and repeat the example above until no cubes are left.
- Work through the example in the textbook together.

## Additional activity

Display pictures of flowers, toy cars, sandwiches, etc. on the board (not more than 10 items each). Ask pupils to count the number of items and say the numbers out loud. Ask pupils to write the number words.

Numbers to 10 **Unit 1**

## Activity

**3** **a** Count the things. How many are there?

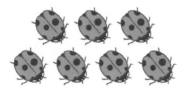

7

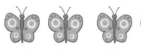

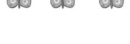

7

7

**b** Work in pairs.

Show your partner 10 .

Show your partner 10 .

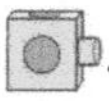

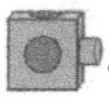

Show your partner any 10 things around you.

9

## Teaching sequence

**3**

**a**

- Ask pupils to count the same number of items using different objects. Ask them to write '7' for each set of objects.

  Now ask pupils to name any 7 objects they can see around them.

**b**

- Ask pupils to work together in pairs. Ask each pupil to put 10 cubes on their table and count them.

  Pupils show their 10 cubes and then count the items together.

## Teaching sequence

- Ask pupils to count and write the number of objects. Use this to assess pupil's understanding.
- Look for pupils using counting during role playing or dice games. You can support pupils who need additional practice by encouraging them to join in with your counting and scribe the results.

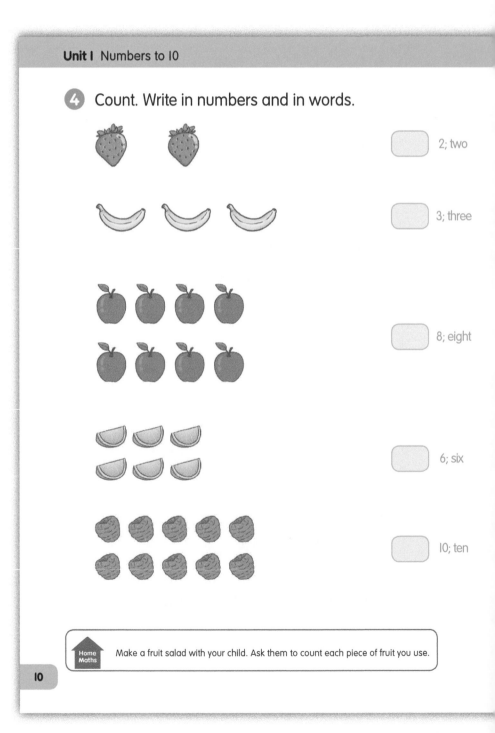

**Unit I** Numbers to 10

④ Count. Write in numbers and in words.

2; two

3; three

8; eight

6; six

10; ten

Home Maths   Make a fruit salad with your child. Ask them to count each piece of fruit you use.

10

8   **Unit I:** Numbers to 10

## Additional activity

Give each pupil a blank piece of paper. Describe a scene for pupils to draw using the numbers 1 to 10.

E.g.  Jack went to the playground and saw 3 boys. (Pupils to draw 3 boys.)

Continue describing or ask pupils to describe (2 girls, 2 see-saws, 4 swings, 2 slides, etc).

Encourage pupils to share their drawings with the class.

**5**  Count the things in the picture.
How many are there?

 10    6    3   8

## Teaching sequence

**5**

Ask pupils to count the number of items.

11

**What you will need**
Photocopy master I (see page 253)

**Independent work**
Practice I in Practice Book IA, pp 5 to I2.

## Teaching sequence

**6** *Game*

- Ask pupils to work in groups of 3. Model how to play the game.
- A pupil starts counting from I. They have to show the corresponding number of fingers while counting. They can use only I to 3 fingers in their turn. The rest of the pupils take turns to count aloud from the number given by the previous pupil. Likewise they can use only I to 3 fingers in their turns. The aim is to be the first to reach I0.

**Example:**
Player I (starts): *I, 2* (using 2 fingers)
Player 2 (continues): *3, 4, 5* (using 3 fingers)
Player 3 (carries on): *6, 7, 8* (using 3 fingers)
Player I (wins): *9, I0* (using 2 fingers)

- Ask pupils to share their strategies.
- Suggest to pupils that a good strategy is to vary the number of fingers used.

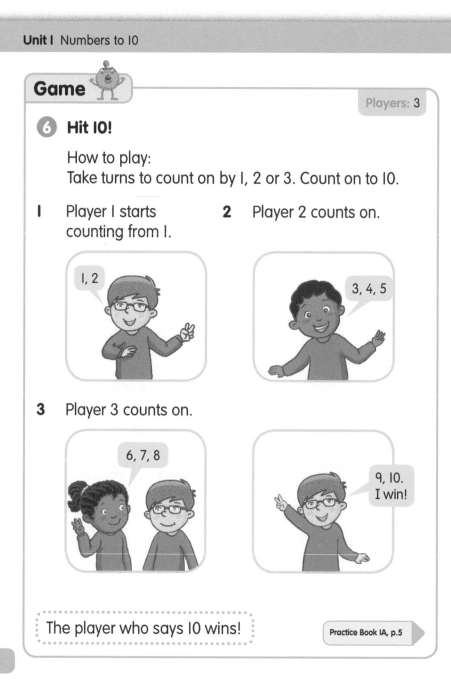

Unit I  Numbers to 10

**Game**

Players: 3

**6** **Hit I0!**

How to play:
Take turns to count on by I, 2 or 3. Count on to I0.

I  Player I starts counting from I.

*I, 2*

2  Player 2 counts on.

*3, 4, 5*

3  Player 3 counts on.

*6, 7, 8*

*9, I0. I win!*

The player who says I0 wins!

Practice Book IA, p.5

I2

## Learning objectives: Compare

**Pupils will be able to:**

- compare two sets of objects (using the method of one-to-one correspondence) and identify the set that has more, fewer or the same number of objects
- use the terms 'more than' and 'fewer than' when comparing two sets of objects
- compare two numbers using the terms 'greater than' or 'smaller than'

## Key concepts

- Two sets of objects can be compared using the method of one-to-one correspondence.
- The number of objects can be the same as, smaller than or greater than another set of objects.

## What you will need

10 counters, such as cubes or apples

## Additional activity

Show pupils how to compare two sets of counters.

---

# Let's Learn!

### Compare

1 Match and compare.

There are 4 children.
There are 4 apples.
The number of children and the number of apples are **the same**.

2 Match and compare.

There are **more** children **than** apples.
There are **fewer** apples **than** children.

13

## Teaching sequence

**1**

- Invite volunteers to stand in front of the class.
- Show pupils an equal number of counters.
- Encourage pupils to count the number of volunteers and counters separately.
- Distribute the counters by matching each volunteer to a counter.
- Look for pupils who notice that each volunteer has a counter.
- Emphasise the word 'same'. Say: "*The number of children and the number of apples are the same.*"

**2**

- Collect the counters from the volunteers. Then ask one more volunteer to join the original group.
- Redistribute the counters. There will be one volunteer without a counter.
- Ask pupils if every volunteer has a counter. Use the words 'more than' and 'fewer than' to describe the volunteers and the counters.
- Work through the example in the textbook together.

**Additional activity**

Invite a volunteer to hold up a few fingers and ask pupils to show more fingers or fewer fingers.

**Examples:**

Say:
"Miya is holding up 3 fingers. Hold up more fingers than Miya."

"Omar is holding up 9 fingers. Hold up fewer fingers than Omar."

## Teaching sequence

- Show two sets of counters. One of the sets should have fewer counters than the other. Ask pupils to match counters from one set to those in the other set. Encourage them to describe the sets of counters using the words 'more' and 'fewer'.
- Work through the example in the textbook together.

- Look for pupils who use 'more than' and 'fewer than' appropriately.
- Play clapping and hopping games together. Say: "Can you say whether you did more than or fewer than 6 hops?"

Unit 1 Numbers to 10

Match and compare.
Say if there are **more** or **fewer**.

③

There are [ more ] socks than shoes.

There are [ fewer ] shoes than socks.

④

There are [ more ] cats than fish.

There are [ fewer ] dogs than fish.

More or fewer?

## Activity

**5** This is a number train.

1 Make a number train with more than 3 .
How many  are there in your train? 4 or more

2 Make a number train with fewer than 3 .
How many  are there in your train? 1 or 2

3 Make a number train with more than 7 .
How many  are there in your train? 8 or more

4 Make a number train with fewer than 7 .
How many  are there in your train? 1, 2, 3, 4, 5 or 6

**6** Count and compare.

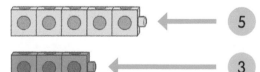 ←— 5

←— 3

5 is **greater than** 3.
3 is **smaller than** 5.

 **Home Maths** Explain to your child that 'greater than' is a mathematical term. It means 'bigger than'. Compare sets of objects at home.

15

## Teaching sequence

**5**

• Show pupils how to use cubes to make a number train.

• Ask pupils to work in groups to make a 3-cube train.

• Ask pupils to make a train with more cubes than the 3-cube train. Ask each group: *"How long is your train?"*

• Ask pupils to make a train with fewer cubes than the 3-cube train. Ask each group: *"How long is your train?"*

• Ask pupils to make a train with more cubes than a 7-cube train. Ask each group: *"How long is your train?"*

• Ask pupils to make a train with fewer cubes than the 7-cube train. Ask each group: *"How long is your train?"*

**6**

• Encourage pupils to compare numbers using the words 'greater than' and 'smaller than'.

• Encourage pupils to relate the numbers to concrete objects. Say:
*"5 cubes is more than 3 cubes, so 5 is greater than 3."*
*"3 cubes is fewer than 5 cubes, so 3 is smaller than 5."*

## Teaching sequence

**What you will need**
15 cubes for each group

**Independent work**
Practice 2 in Practice Book IA, pp 13 to 18.

- Look for pupils who can compare 6 cubes with 8 cubes.

- Ask pupils to work in groups. Ask each group to make two number trains using 4 cubes and 9 cubes.
- Ask pupils which train has more or fewer cubes. Then ask them to write down which number is greater or smaller.

- Ask pupils to find the greater number. Look for pupils who can relate the numbers 8 and 5 to the corresponding number of cubes.

- Ask pupils to find the smaller number. Look for pupils who can find the smaller number and relate the numbers 6 and 9 to the corresponding number of cubes.

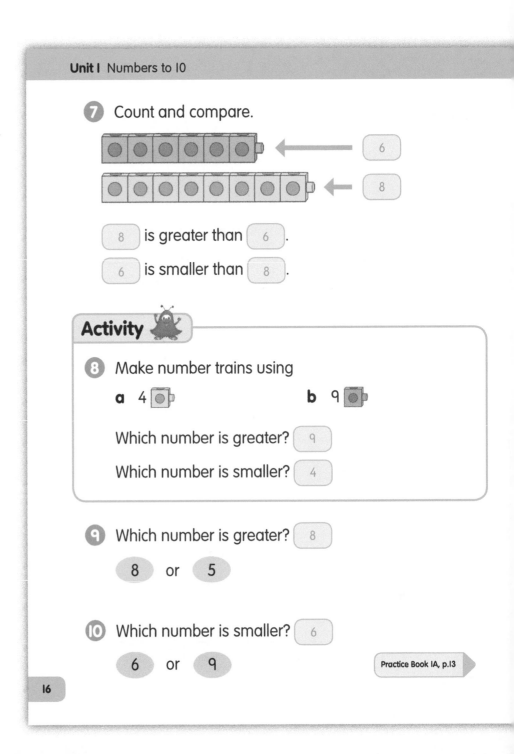

**Unit I** Numbers to 10

**7** Count and compare.

6

8

8 is greater than 6 .

6 is smaller than 8 .

**Activity**

**8** Make number trains using

a 4

b 9

Which number is greater? 9

Which number is smaller? 4

**9** Which number is greater? 8

8 or 5

**10** Which number is smaller? 6

6 or 9

Practice Book IA, p.13

16

## Learning objectives: Order and pattern

**Pupils will be able to:**

- compare the number of items from a sequence of objects and find the number of objects in a sequence
- interpret and use statements containing 'I more than' or 'I less than' a given number

## Key concept

A sequence of objects and numbers can form a pattern.

## What you will need

- 15 cubes
- Abacus

## Let's Learn!

### Order and pattern

1 Jack makes this pattern:

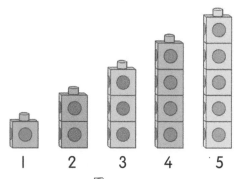

| | | | | |
|---|---|---|---|---|
| I | 2 | 3 | 4 | 5 |

How many  come next in the pattern?

I, 2, 3, 4, 5, **6**

6  come next in the pattern.

2 Ella makes a pattern with beads.

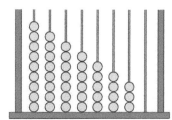

How many beads come next in the pattern? ( 2 )

17

## Teaching sequence

**1**

- Arrange a set of cubes in the pattern. Ask pupils to compare the number of cubes in the first and second columns. Ask them to find the difference.
- Ask pupils to compare the number of cubes in the second and third columns, third and fourth columns, and fourth and fifth columns.
- Write out the number sequence and show pupils that the next column should have 6 cubes.

**2**

- Show pupils an abacus, with beads arranged in the pattern. Ask them to compare the number of beads in one column with the number of beads in the next column. Ask them to find the difference.
- Encourage pupils to look for the pattern.
- Ask pupils to write down the number of beads that come next.

## Thinking skills

- Comparing
- Sequencing

## What you will need

30 cubes for each group

## Additional activity

Ask pupils to make their own patterns using different numbers and cubes.

## Teaching sequence

- Arrange a set of cubes in the pattern from 2 to 4. Ask pupils how the set of cubes shows a pattern.
- Ask pupils to work in groups. Ask each group to make a pattern using 4 to 7 cubes and 6 to 9 cubes.

- Look for pupils who can explain the pattern. For pupils who need additional support, say: *"I think your pattern increases by one more cube each time. Am I right?"*

### Activity

3 Use 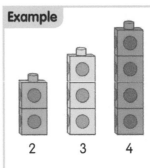 to make a set of towers.

**Example**

2      3      4

This shows a pattern from 2 to 4.

Use  to show:

**a** a pattern from 4 to 7

**b** a pattern from 9 to 6

4 Count to find the next number.

I, 2, 3, 4, [ 5 ]

18

**5** Complete the number patterns.

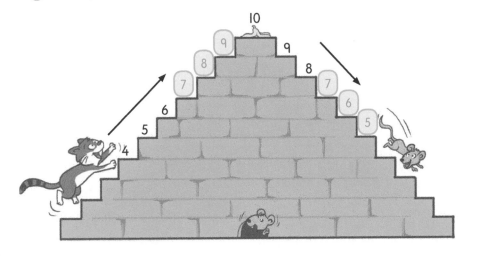

**6** What is I **more than** 3?

3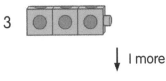

↓ I more

4

4 is I more than 3.

**7** What is I **more than** 6?

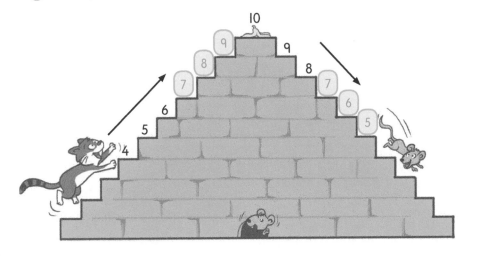

7 is I more than 6.

19

## Teaching sequence

- Look for pupils who can describe the number patterns.

- Explain the meaning of 'I more than another number'. Say: "I more than 3 means add I on to the number."
- Ask pupils to work in groups. Ask each group to join 3 cubes and I cube to show 'I more than'.

- Look for pupils who can use 'I more than' appropriately. Encourage pupils to use cubes to check their answer.

**Independent work**

Practice 3 in Practice Book IA, pp 19 to 22.

**What you will need**

10 cubes for each group

## Teaching sequence

- Explain the meaning of 'I less than another number'. Say: *"I less than another number means take away I from the number."*
- Ask pupils to work in groups. Ask each group to remove I cube from 4 cubes to show 'I less than'.

- Look for pupils who can describe their train using 'I less than'. Encourage pupils to use cubes to check their answer.

- Encourage pupils to use 'I more than' and 'I less than' to complete the number patterns.

**(II)** *Maths Journal*

- Ask pupils to reflect on these concepts:
  - Number of items (e.g. wheels) on an object
  - When do we use 'smaller than' or 'less than'?

---

Unit I **Numbers to 10**

**8** What is I **less than** 4?

4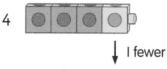

↓ I fewer

3

3 is I less than 4.

**9** What is I **less than** 6?

⌜ 5 ⌟ is I less than ⌜ 6 ⌟.

**10** Complete the number patterns.

a  2, 3, 4, ⌜ 5 ⌟, ⌜ 6 ⌟, 7, 8

b  10, 9, ⌜ 8 ⌟, ⌜ 7 ⌟, ⌜ 6 ⌟, 5, 4

Practice Book IA, p.19

### Maths Journal

**II** Which of these sentences are correct?

a  A bicycle has 2 wheels. ✔

b  A triangle has 3 sides. ✔

c  7 is smaller than 5.

d  8 is I less than 9. ✔

20

---

## Heuristic for problem solving
Looking for patterns and relationships

## What you will need
Photocopy master 2 (see page 254)

## Independent work
*Challenging Practice* and *Problem Solving* in Practice Book IA, pp 23 to 24.

## Maths Journal

12 Write about the picture using the numbers 1 to 10.

**Example**

There are 6 chairs.

## Put On Your Thinking Caps!

13 Look at these number discs.

7  3  2  6  10  9  4  5  1  8

Put each disc in the correct box.

| Numbers smaller than 5 | Numbers from 5 to 7 | Numbers greater than 7 |
|---|---|---|
| 1, 2, 3, 4 | 5, 6, 7 | 8, 9, 10 |

What can you say about the colours of the discs in each group?
They are the same colour.

Practice Book IA, p.23 ▸    Practice Book IA, p.24 ▸

21

## Teaching sequence

12 *Maths Journal*

- Some possible answers are:
  There is 1 table.
  There are 3 cups.
  There are 2 cakes.
  There are 4 biscuits.

13 *Put On Your Thinking Caps!*

- Ask pupils to put the numbers into the correct groups.
- Encourage pupils to look for patterns in the groups.

# INSPIRE MATHS

# PRACTICE BOOK 1A

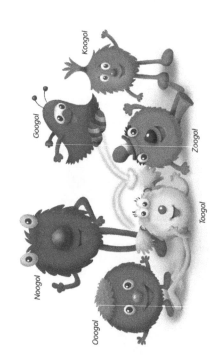

Noogol   Ooogol   Toogol   Zoogol   Googol   Koogol

Consultant and author
Dr Fong Ho Kheong

Authors
Chelvi Ramakrishnan and Bernice Lau Pui Wah

UK consultants
Carole Skinner, Simon d'Angelo and Elizabeth Gibbs

---

Date: _____

## Unit 1   Numbers to I0

Practice I   **Counting to I0**

I   Count the things. Write the number.

Example

    2 rabbits

a     3 snails

b     7 pears

c     I0 carrots

**3** Draw:

**a** 2 horns on each bull.

**b** 4 legs on each chair.

**c** 6 legs on each ant.

**d** 10 spots on each dog.

---

**2** How many animals are there?

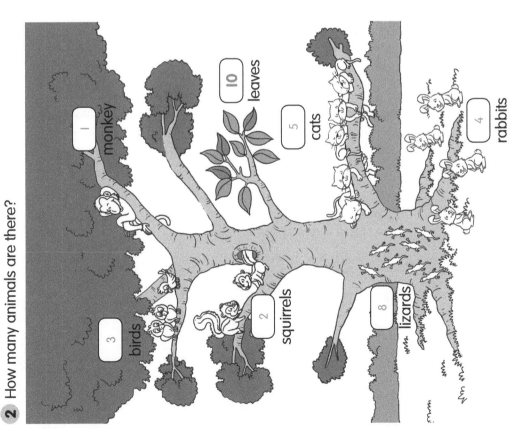

birds 3

monkey 1

10 leaves

squirrels 2

5 cats

lizards 8

rabbits 4

**5** Count the things on the snowman.

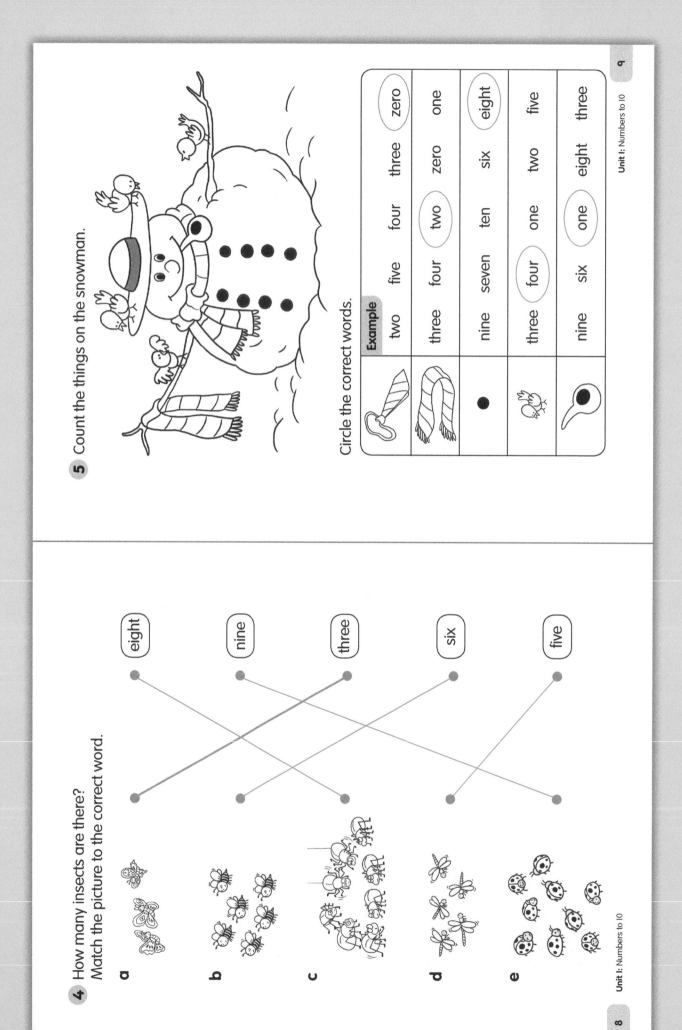

Circle the correct words.

| | Example | | | | |
|---|---|---|---|---|---|
| (scarf) | two | five | four | three | (zero) |
| (scarf) | three | four | (two) | zero | one |
| ● | nine | seven | ten | six | (eight) |
| (bird) | three | (four) | one | two | five |
| ● | nine | six | (one) | eight | three |

**4** How many insects are there?
Match the picture to the correct word.

a

b

c

d

e

eight

nine

three

six

five

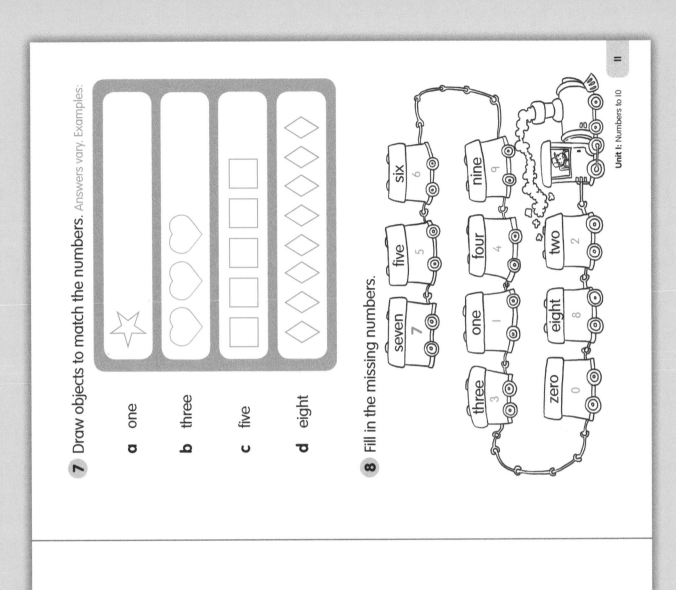

**6** Match the numbers to the correct words.

3 — zero

10 — seven

0 — nine

7 — three

2 — two

4 — four

9 — ten

**7** Draw objects to match the numbers. Answers vary. Examples:

**a** one

**b** three

**c** five

**d** eight

**8** Fill in the missing numbers.

seven 7    five 5    six 6

three 3    one I    four 4    nine 9

zero 0    eight 8    two 2

**Practice 2** Compare

1 Which sets have the same number of objects?
Circle them.

**Example**

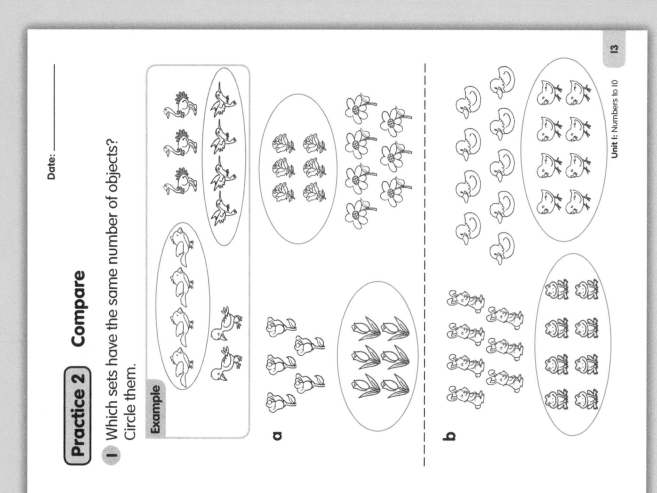

a

b

9 Fill in the missing words.

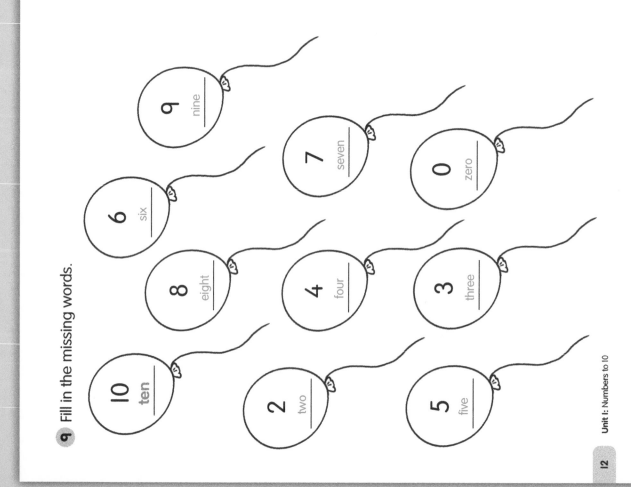

| | |
|---|---|
| 10 ten | 6 six | 9 nine |
| 8 eight | 7 seven | |
| 2 two | 4 four | |
| 5 five | 3 three | 0 zero |

**2** Are there more, fewer or the same?
Match to find out. Then fill in the spaces.

Example

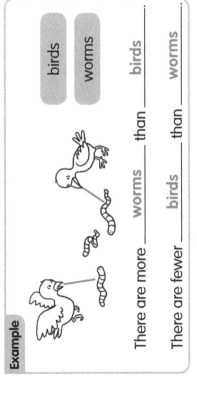

birds    worms

There are more _worms_ than _birds_ .

There are fewer _birds_ than _worms_ .

**a**

birds    nests    same

There are _5_ birds.

There are _5_ nests.

The number of _birds_ and the number of _nests_ are the _same_ .

**b**

hats    children

There are more _hats_ than _children_ .

There are fewer _children_ than _hats_ .

**c**

big    small    same

How many big eggs are there? _4_

How many small eggs are there? _4_

The number of _big_ eggs and the number of _small_ eggs are the _same_ .

## Page 16

**3** Which two sets have the same number of objects?

Join them to a ▢.

Write the number in the ▢.

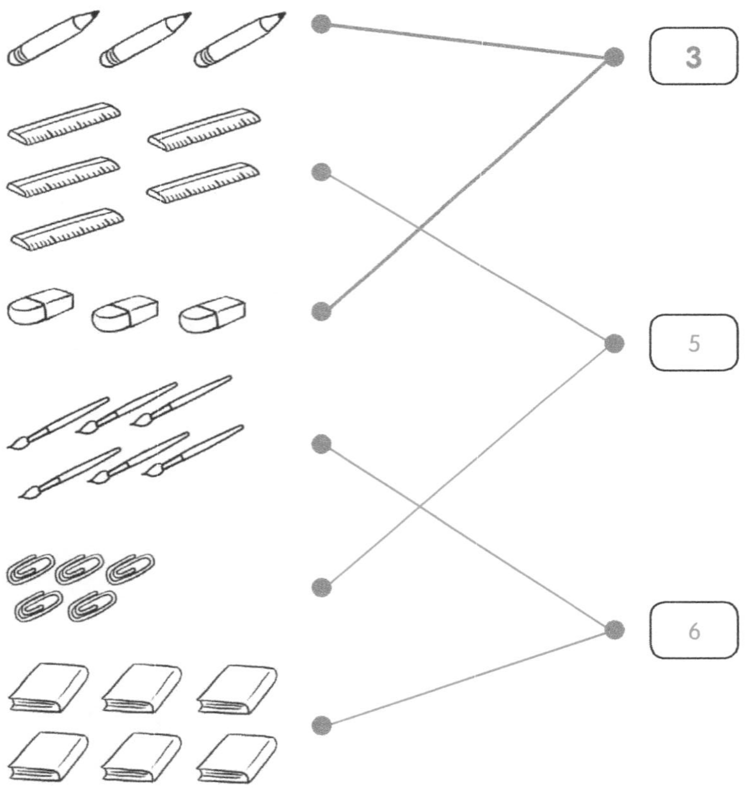

| 3 |
| 5 |
| 6 |

## Page 17

**4** Count the objects. Fill in the spaces and circle the correct objects.

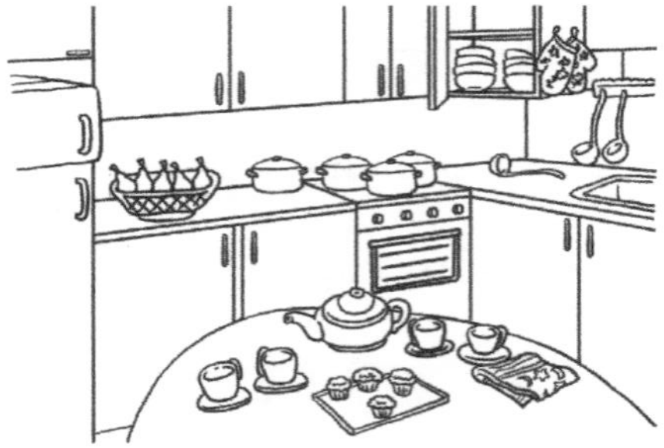

Are there more 🫖 or more 🍐?

| 4 | | 5 |

**a** Are there more 🍶 or more 🫖?

____ 4

**b** Are there fewer 🍶 or fewer 🧁?

8 ____

**c** Are there fewer 🍪 or fewer 🥚?

2 ____ 4

cups 🌰   bowls 🍚   teapots 🫖   pots 🫕

There are the same number of ____ cups ____ and ____ pots ____.

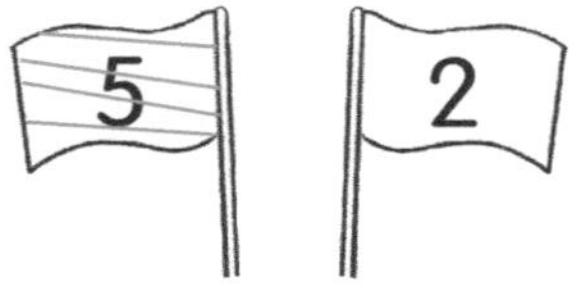

Date: _____

## Practice 3  Order and pattern

**1** What comes next?

a  6 7 8 9 10

b 4 3 2 1 0

c 3 4 5 6 7

**2** What is 1 more?

a  8 9 10

b  6 7 8

c  3 4 5

---

**5** Colour the sign with the smaller number.

a 5   10

b 9

c 7   3

d 1

e 2   0

f 9

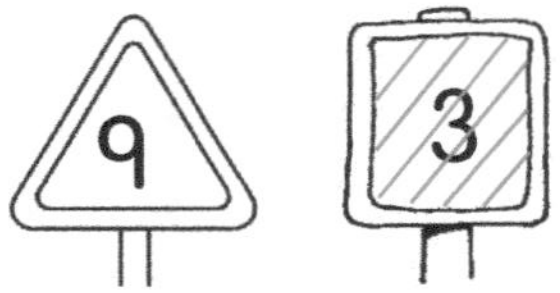

**6** Colour the flag with the greater number.

a 0   10

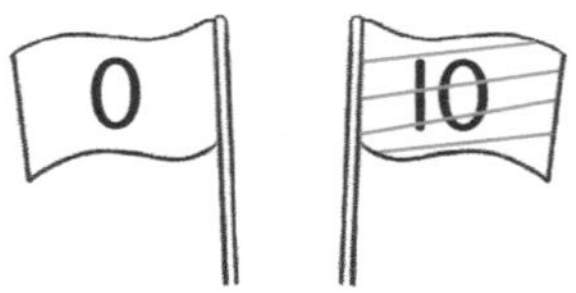

b 8   6

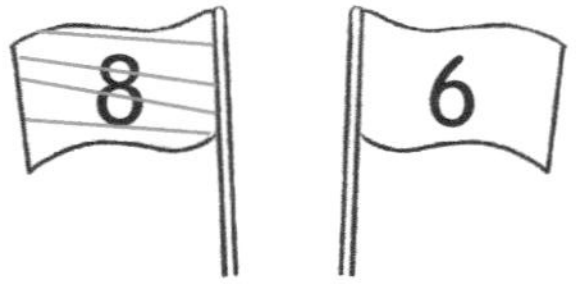

c 5   2

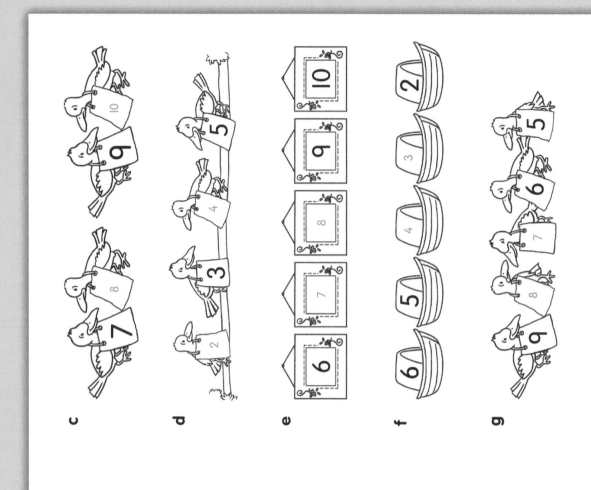

c

d

e

f

g

**3** What is I less?
Write the number.

a    3    2    1

b    6    5    4

c    2    1    0

**4** Complete the number patterns.

a    4    5    6    7    8

b    0    1    2    3    4

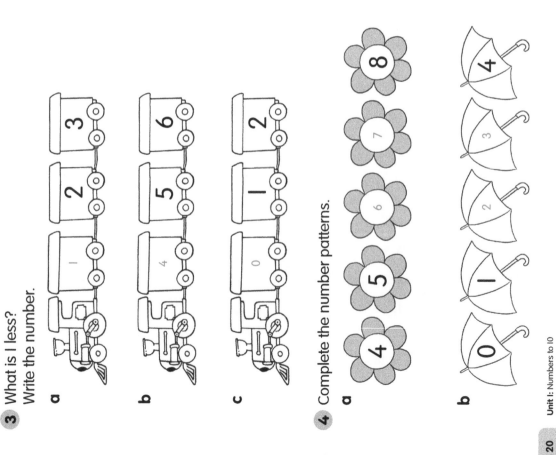

Date: _____

## Challenging Practice

The hen has lost her eggs.
Her eggs have numbers that are more than 2 and less than 8.
Colour the eggs that belong to the hen.

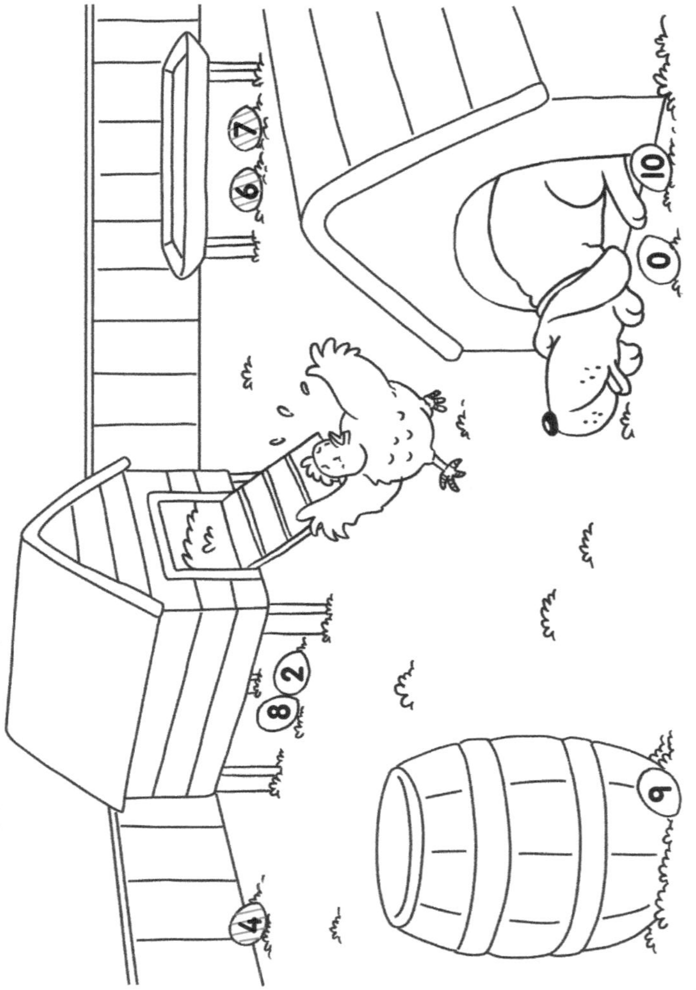

---

**5** Fill in the spaces.

a   1 more than 4 is ___5___.

b   1 more than 8 is ___9___.

c   1 more than 5 is ___6___.

d   1 less than 5 is ___4___.

e   1 less than 9 is ___8___.

f   1 less than 6 is ___5___.

g   ___4___ is 1 more than 3.

h   ___7___ is 1 more than 6.

i   ___3___ is 1 less than 4.

j   ___6___ is 1 less than 7.

Date: _____

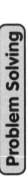

△  △△△  △△△△△

1  Peter sees a pattern made with △.

Help Peter to carry on the pattern.

Draw the next group of △ in the box.

△△△△△△△

There are ___7___ △ in the next group.

Unit I: Numbers to I0

# Unit 2: Number Bonds

| Week | Learning Objectives | Thinking Skills | Resources |
|---|---|---|---|
| 3 | **Making number bonds**<br><br>Pupils will be able to:<br>• use cubes to show number bonds for numbers up to 10<br>• use a number balance to show number bonds for numbers from 6 to 10<br>• investigate all possible sets of two numbers that make a given number<br>• investigate all possible sets of three numbers that make a given number<br><br>*Let's Explore!*<br>Pupils will be able to show all possible combinations of three numbers that make a given number such as 9 or 10.<br><br>*Maths Journal*<br>Pupils will be able to recall number bonds and relate them to situations. | • Analysing parts and whole<br><br>Heuristic for problem solving:<br>• Guess and check | • Pupil Textbook IA, pp 22 to 26<br>• Practice Book IA, pp 25 to 34<br>• Teacher's Guide IA, pp 32 to 36 |
| 3 | *Put On Your Thinking Caps!*<br>Pupils will be able to make deductions and apply number bonds to solve problems.<br><br>Review 1 | • Analysing parts and whole<br>• Comparing<br>• Deduction | • Pupil Textbook IA, p 27<br>• Practice Book IA, pp 35 to 36<br>• Teacher's Guide IA, p 37 |
| **Summative assessment opportunity** | | | • Practice Book IA, pp 37 to 40 |

Assessment Book I, Test I, pp 1 to 7

# Number Bonds

## Learning objectives: Making number bonds

**Pupils will be able to:**

- use cubes to show number bonds for numbers up to 10
- use a number balance to show number bonds for numbers from 6 to 10
- investigate all possible sets of two numbers that make a given number
- investigate all possible sets of three numbers that make a given number

## Key concept

Adding two or more numbers gives another number.

## What you will need

15 cubes (3 colours: 5 cubes of each colour)

## Teaching sequence

**a**

- Make a number train with 4 cubes. Count aloud the number of cubes. Then separate 1 cube from the train to make 2 groups of cubes. Ask pupils to count aloud the number of cubes in each group.
- **Tip:** For pupils who need additional support, use 3 cubes of one colour and 1 cube of another colour when making the 4-cube train.
- Write the number bond 3-1—4 on the board. Explain to pupils that the two number bonds, 3-1—4 and 1-3—4, are the same. Explain that number bonds are different combinations of numbers that make up a number. Each number bond represents a 'part-whole' relationship between three numbers.

---

### Unit 2 Number Bonds

**Let's Learn!**

**Making number bonds**

**Activity**

**1 a** You will need ⬡⬡⬡⬡.
Put the cubes into two groups.

**Example**

How many are there in each group?

whole **4** — part **3**
— part **1**

3 and 1 make 4.

22

## Thinking skill
Analysing parts and whole

## Heuristic for problem solving
Guess and check

## What you will need
- 15 cubes (3 colours: 5 cubes of each colour)
- 10 cubes for each group
- Photocopy master 3 (see pages 255 and 256)

## Additional activity
Ask pupils to work in groups to make all the number bonds for 6. Each group will need 12 cubes.

## Teaching sequence

**①**

**b**

- Ask pupils to explore other ways in which the 4 cubes can be separated into 2 groups. Encourage pupils to experiment with possible ways and to write the number bonds on the board.

**②** **a and b**

- Ask pupils to work in groups. Ask each group to find all the possible combinations of numbers that make 5. For pupils who need additional support, suggest that they begin with number bonds for 1.
- Encourage pupils to discuss their answers.

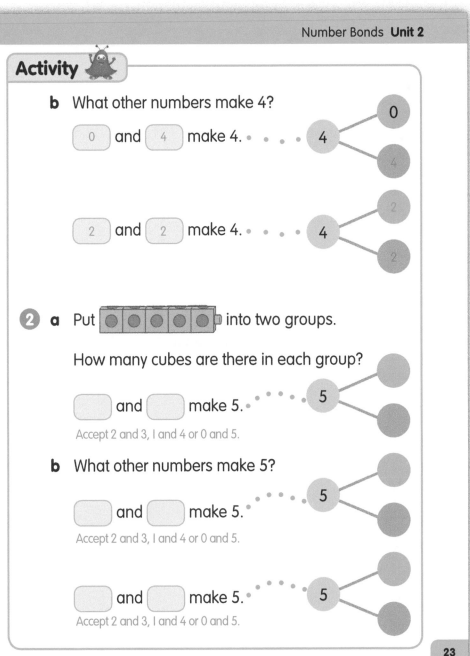

### Activity

**b** What other numbers make 4?

[ 0 ] and [ 4 ] make 4. • • • • • 4 — 0
                                        — 4

[ 2 ] and [ 2 ] make 4. • • • • • 4 — 2
                                        — 2

**②** **a** Put  into two groups.

How many cubes are there in each group?

[  ] and [  ] make 5. • • • • • 5
Accept 2 and 3, 1 and 4 or 0 and 5.

**b** What other numbers make 5?

[  ] and [  ] make 5. • • • • • 5
Accept 2 and 3, 1 and 4 or 0 and 5.

[  ] and [  ] make 5. • • • • • 5
Accept 2 and 3, 1 and 4 or 0 and 5.

23

## What you will need

- Number balance
- 3 weights

## Suggestion

For pupils who need additional support, start by demonstrating using cubes before proceeding to the number balance.

## Independent work

Practices I to 3 in Practice Book IA, pp 25 to 34.

## Teaching sequence

a

- Show pupils the number balance, and explain that when 3 weights (2 weights on one side and I weight on the other side) are placed on it, and the balance is level, it means that the 3 numbers form a number bond.
- Show pupils how to make a number bond for 7 (3-4—7) by placing weights at 7 on one side, and at 3 and 4 on the other side. Write the number bond on the board.

b

- Remove the weights at 3 and 4 but keep the weight at 7. Ask pupils to think of other numbers that can make the balance level. Invite volunteers to use the number balance to check their answers. Write the number bonds on the board.

### Activity

**3** **a** Make number bonds of 7 with a number balance.

3 and 4 make 7. • • • • • • • • • • • • 7 — 3, 4

**b** What other numbers make 7?

? ?

7 — I, 6        7 — 2, 5        7 — 7, 0

Practice Book IA, pp. 25, 29 and 31

24

## Objective of activity

Pupils will be able to show all possible combinations of three numbers that make a given number such as 9 or 10.

## Thinking skill

Analysing parts and whole

## Heuristic for problem solving

Guess and check

## What you will need

- 1 number balance for each group
- 3 weights for each group
- Photocopy master 4 (see pages 257 and 258)

## Let's Explore!

④ Use  or a number balance.

**a** Find three numbers that make 9.

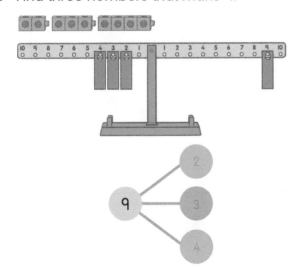

Think of two more ways to do this.

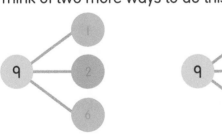

**b** Find three numbers that make 10. Think of two more ways to do this.

Answers can be 1, 2, 7; 1, 3, 6; 1, 4, 5; 2, 3, 5.

25

## Teaching sequence

④ *Let's Explore!*

**a**

- Ask pupils to work in groups. Ask each group to investigate all possible combinations of 3 numbers that make 9 with the help of the number balance.

**b**

- Ask pupils to work on all the possible number bonds for 10.
- Ask each group to write their number bonds on the board and use the number balance to explain their answers.

## Objective of activity

Pupils will be able to recall number bonds and relate them to situations.

## Additional activity

Ask pupils to work in groups. Ask each group to tell a story involving objects/people. Use numbers up to 10.

## Teaching sequence

**5** *Maths Journal*

- Encourage pupils to relate the picture with number bonds.
- Encourage pupils to think of their own examples involving stools of different colours, boys and girls, etc.

## Objective of activity

Pupils will be able to make deductions and apply number bonds to solve problems.

## Thinking skills

- Analysing parts and whole
- Comparing
- Deduction

## Independent work

*Challenging Practice, Problem Solving* and Review I in Practice Book IA, pp 35 to 40.

## Additional activity

Ask pupils to work in pairs. One pupil has a set of counters (not more than I0). They tell their partner the number of counters. Next they hide some counters under a cup and show the rest to their partner. Their partner says how many counters are under the cup. Each pair takes turns to hide the counters.

## Teaching sequence

⑥ *Put On Your Thinking Caps!*

- Look for pupils who can relate number bonds with the covered and uncovered beads.
- Encourage pupils to solve the problems by saying:
  *"How many beads are there altogether?"*
  *"How many beads do you see?"*
  *"How many beads are there under the cup?"*
- Encourage pupils to recall the number bonds they know.

# Put On Your Thinking Caps!

⑥ How many beads are hidden?

**a** There are 6 beads altogether under the two cups.

 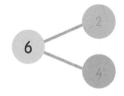

**b** There are 8 beads altogether under the two cups.

 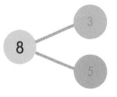

**c** There are I0 beads altogether under the three cups.

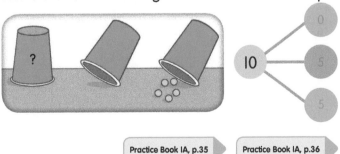

> Practice Book IA, p.35    > Practice Book IA, p.36

27

## Unit 2  Number Bonds

Date: _____

### Practice 1    Making number bonds

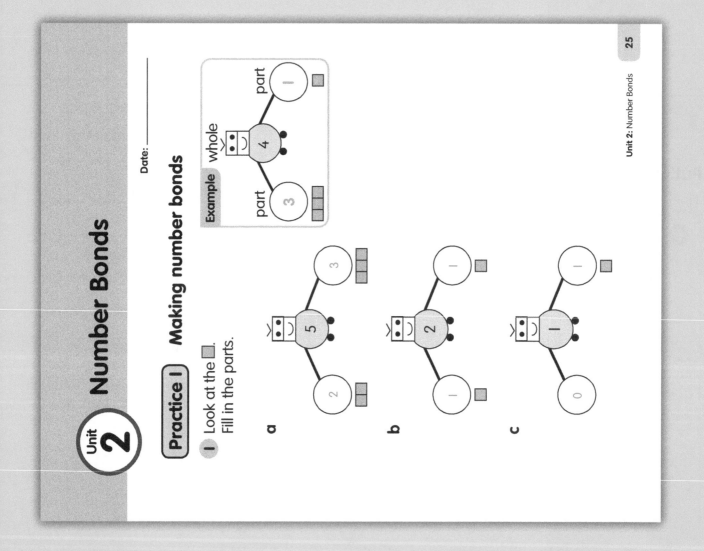

**Example**

whole

4

part — 3

part —

1 Look at the ▢.
Fill in the parts.

a    5    2    3

b    2    —    —

c    —    0    —

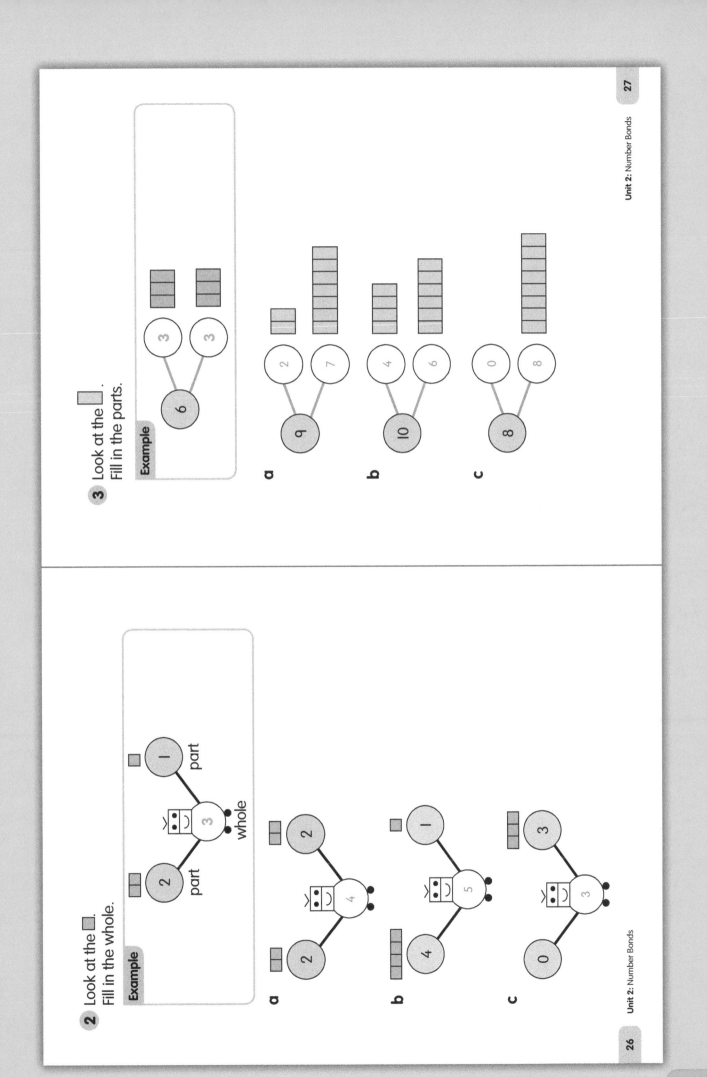

**2** Look at the ▢.
Fill in the whole.

Example

2 part — 3 whole — 1 part

a  2   4   2

b  1   5   4

c  3   3   0

**3** Look at the ▢.
Fill in the parts.

Example

6 — 3  3

a  9 — 2  7

b  10 — 4  6

c  8 — 0  8

**Practice 2**  **Making number bonds**

1  Look at the groups in the pictures.
Complete the number bonds.

**Example**

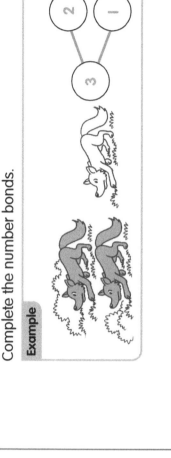

a

b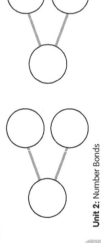

4  Complete the number bonds.

**Example**

10 / 4, 6

____ 4 ____ and ____ 6 ____ make 10.

What other numbers make 10?
Fill in the spaces. Answers vary

a

_____ and _____ make 10.

b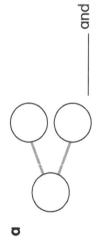

_____ and _____ make 10.

Are there any other numbers that make 10? ____ Yes ____

5  Make number bonds for 8. Answers vary

Date: _____

## Practice 3  Making number bonds

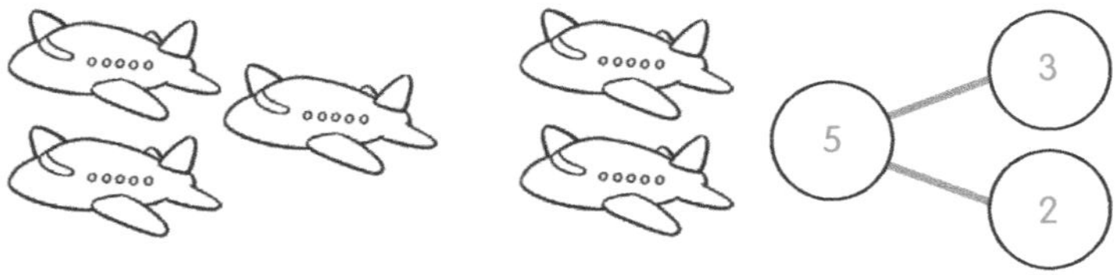

**1** Match to make 8.

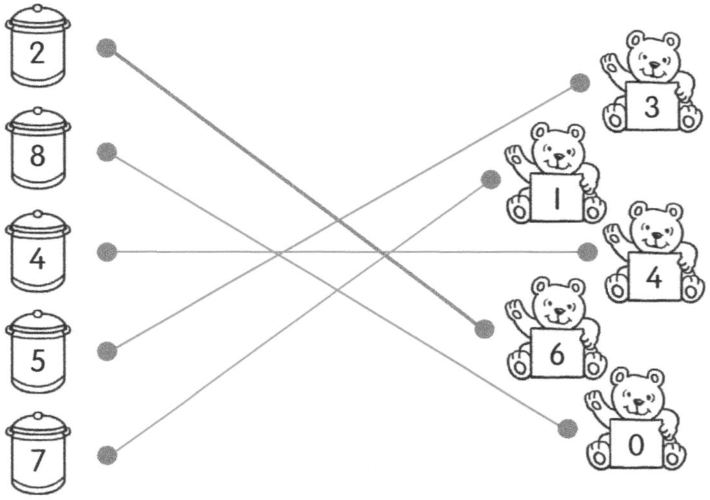

[Number bonds matching: barrels with 2, 8, 4, 5, 7 connected to teddy bears with 3, 1, 4, 6, 0]

**2** Match the numbers.

**a** Match to make 6.

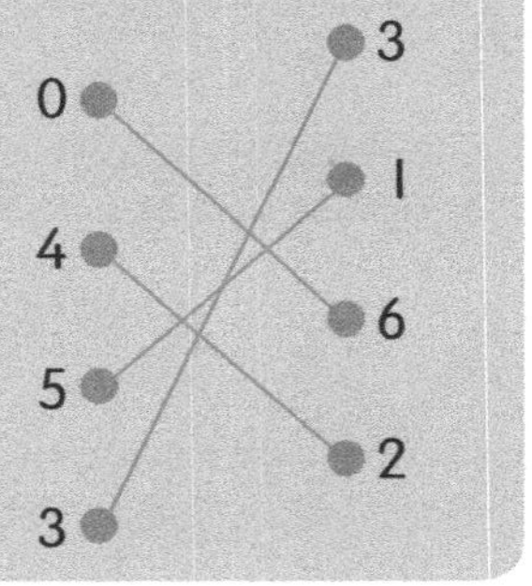

3   1   6   2
0   4   5   3

**b** Match to make 9.

6   5   1   7
8   2   3   4

---

**c**

2   1
3

**d**

3   2
5

**e**

4   3
7

**f**

6   4
10

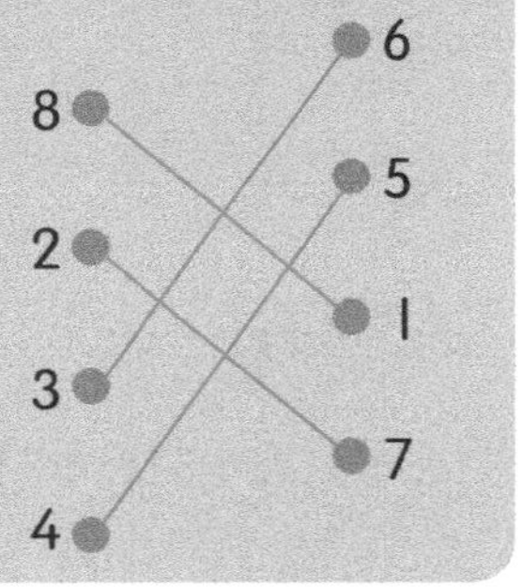

**4** Colour the ☐ to show a pair of numbers that make the number in ◯. Use two colours.

**Example**

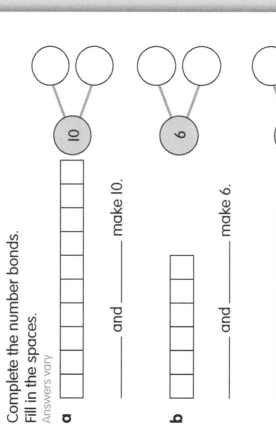

5 and 2 make 7.

Complete the number bonds.
Fill in the spaces.
Answers vary

**a** ___ and ___ make 10.

**b** ___ and ___ make 6.

**c** ___ and ___ make 8.

**3**

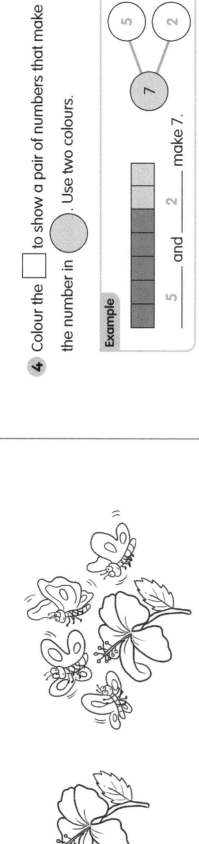

**a** How many butterflies are there around each flower? How many butterflies are there altogether? Complete the number bond to show your answer.

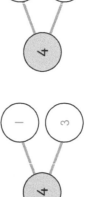

**b** What other numbers make 4? Complete the number bonds.

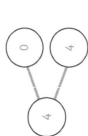

## Challenging Practice

1 Fill in  with numbers from the bag.

Use each number once. Answers vary

a

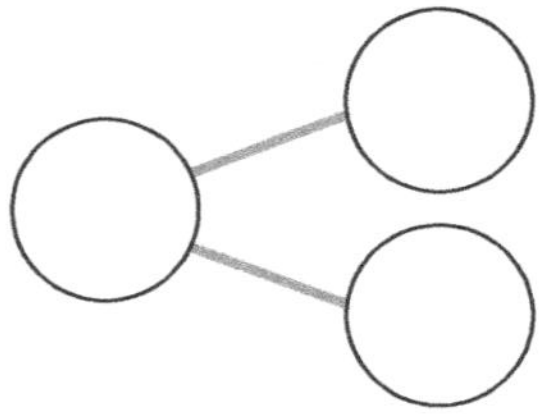

b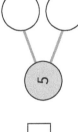

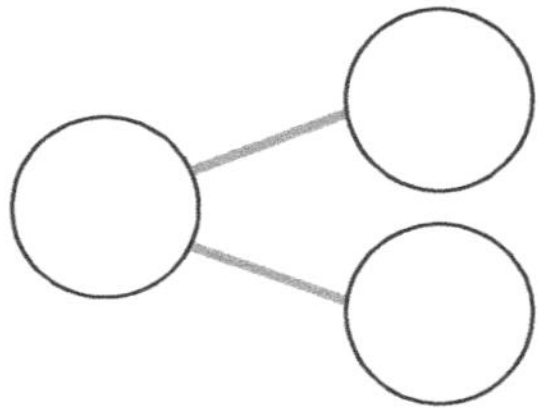

---

5 Colour the ▢ to show a pair of numbers that make 5.

Use two colours.
Complete the number bonds.
Fill in the spaces.

Answers vary

a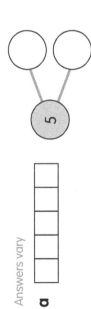

_____ and _____ make 5.

b

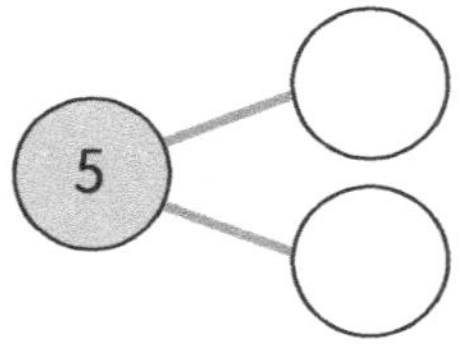

_____ and _____ make 5.

c

_____ and _____ make 5.

Date: _____

# Review I

**1** Count the things. Fill in the spaces.

**a**

There are __6__ ducks.

**b**

There are __9__ dogs and cats altogether.

**2** Write in words.

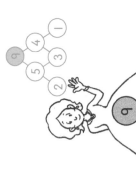

seven

nine

four

five

eight

---

Date: _____

**Problem Solving**

**1** Use numbers from 1 to 10 to complete the number bonds.
Use each number once for each dress.

Example

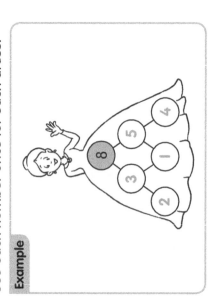

**a**

**b**

**4** Colour the fish with the smaller number.

a  6   10

b   2   9

**5** Colour the fish with the greater number.

a  0   3

b  5   8

**6** Complete the number patterns.

a 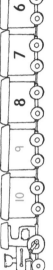 4  5  6  7  8  9  10

b 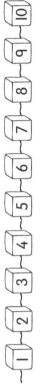 10  9  8  7  6  5

**7** Fill in the spaces.

 1  2  3  4  5  6  7  8  9  10

a  1 more than 5 is ___6___ .

b  1 less than 6 is ___5___ .

c  ___8___ is 1 more than 7.

d  ___6___ is 1 less than 7.

---

**3 a** Circle the group that has more things.

**b** Circle the group that has fewer things.

**c** Circle the groups that have the same number of things.

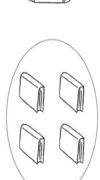
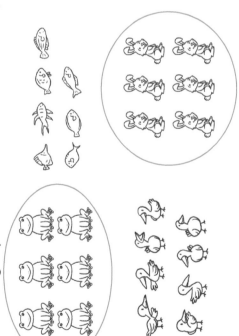

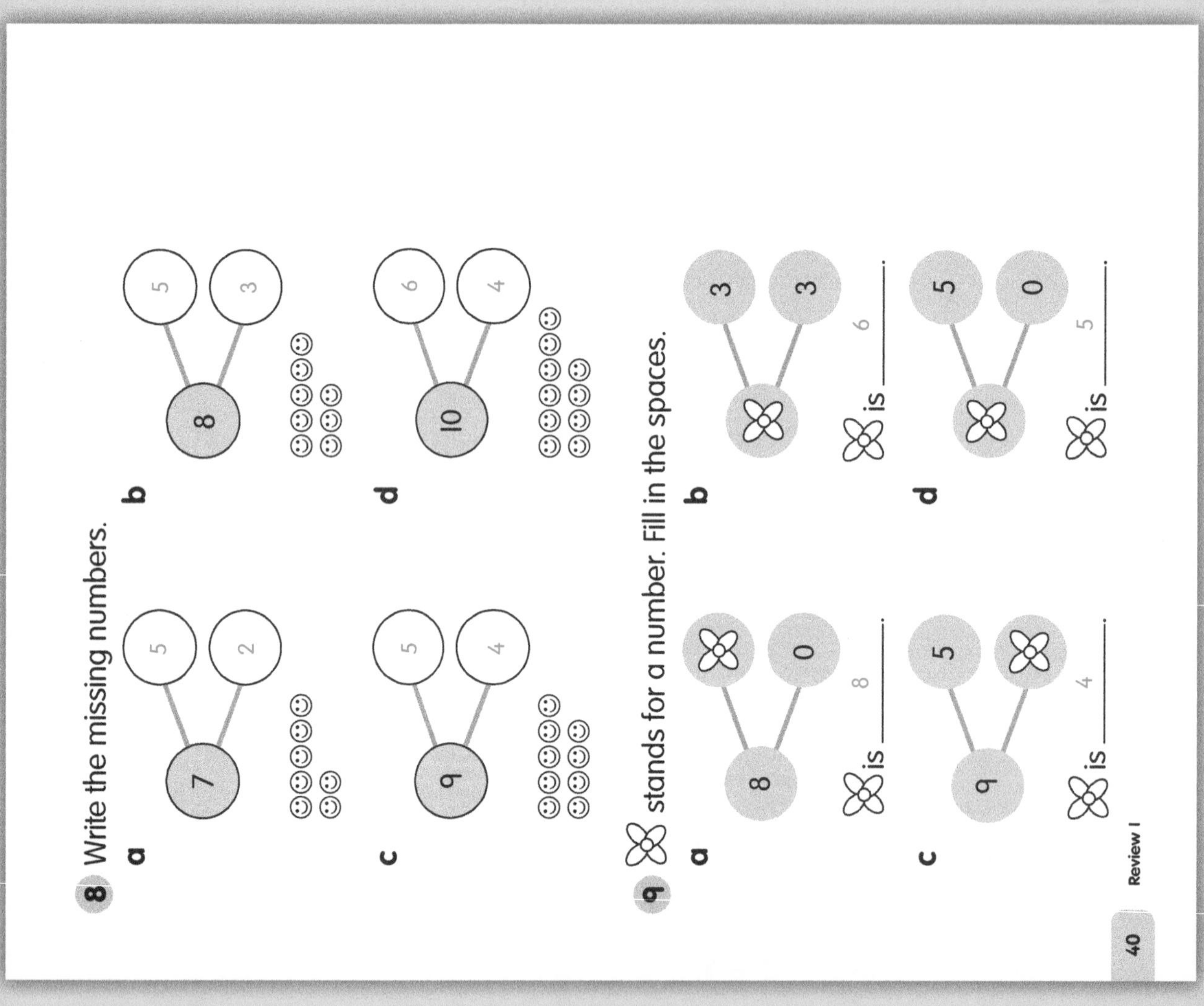

**8** Write the missing numbers.

a 7 — 5, 2

b 8 — 5, 3

c 9 — 5, 4

d 10 — 6, 4

**9** ✿ stands for a number. Fill in the spaces.

a 8 — ✿, 0
✿ is 8.

b ✿ — 3, 3
✿ is 6.

c 9 — 5, ✿
✿ is 4.

d ✿ — 5, 0
✿ is 5.

40 Review 1

# Unit 3: Addition within 10

| Week | Learning Objectives | Thinking Skills | Resources |
|---|---|---|---|
| 4 | **(1) Ways to add**<br><br>Pupils will be able to:<br>• use the 'counting on' strategy to add<br>• relate addition to number bonds<br>• add using number bonds | • Analysing parts and whole | • Pupil Textbook 1A, pp 28 to 33<br>• Practice Book 1A, pp 41 to 50<br>• Teacher's Guide 1A, pp 48 to 53 |
| 4 | **(2) Making addition stories**<br><br>Pupils will be able to make addition stories based on pictures and various situations. | • Analysing parts and whole | • Pupil Textbook 1A, pp 34 to 35<br>• Practice Book 1A, pp 51 to 54<br>• Teacher's Guide 1A, pp 54 to 55 |
| 5 | **(3) Solving word problems**<br><br>Pupils will be able to:<br>• add by recognising two addition concepts: 'part-whole' and 'adding on'<br>• solve addition word problems using number bonds or the 'counting on' strategy | • Analysing parts and whole<br>• Adding on | • Pupil Textbook 1A, pp 36 to 37<br>• Practice Book 1A, pp 55 to 56<br>• Teacher's Guide 1A, pp 56 to 57 |
| 5 | *Put On Your Thinking Caps!*<br><br>Pupils will be able to recall number bonds to solve the problem. | • Deduction<br>• Analysing parts and whole<br><br>Heuristics for problem solving:<br>• Using a diagram<br>• Guess and check | • Pupil Textbook 1A, p 38<br>• Practice Book 1A, pp 57 to 60<br>• Teacher's Guide 1A, p 58 |

# Addition within 10

## Learning objectives:
## Ways to add

**Pupils will be able to:**

- use the 'counting on' strategy to add
- relate addition to number bonds
- add using number bonds

## Key concept

Adding is associated with the 'part-whole' and 'adding on' concepts.

## What you will need

- 10 marbles
- Paper cup
- Marker pen
- 7 button magnets

## Teaching sequence

- Place 5 button magnets on the board. Ask pupils to count the number of button magnets. Then place another 2 button magnets on the board. Ask pupils, "*What is 5 + 2?*" Demonstrate, using the 'counting-on' strategy, how to add 5 and 2.
- Show pupils that to find 6 + 2, they can start counting from the greater number. Put 6 marbles in the paper cup. Write '6' on the paper cup. Now drop 2 more marbles into the cup as you count aloud from 6.
- Write the addition sentence on the board and explain the symbols used.
- Encourage pupils to recall the 'part-whole' relationship between three numbers in a number bond.

---

Unit **3** Addition within 10

Let's Learn!

**Ways to add**

*Adding by counting on*

     $6 + 2 = ?$

Count on from the greater number.
6, **7**, **8**.

$$6 + 2 = 8$$
part   part   whole

+ is called **plus**.
It means **add**.

= means **equals**.

6 + 2 = 8 is an **addition sentence**.
It says **six plus two equals eight**.

28

# Thinking skill

Analysing parts and whole

# What you will need

- 10 marbles
- 2 paper cups
- Marker pen
- 20 cubes in 2 colours (10 of each colour) for each group
- Photocopy master 5 (see page 259)

# Additional activity

When pupils are familiar with the 'counting on' strategy, provide other addition sentences, and encourage them to take turns to make number trains and to demonstrate 'counting on' to one another.

---

**2** Count on from the greater number.

**a** 2 + 5 = ?

5, [ 6 ], [ 7 ]

**5**

**b** 7 + 3 = ?

7, [ 8 ], [ 9 ], [ 10 ]

**7**

## Activity

**3** Make the number trains below.
Count on from the greater number to find the total number of .

**a** 4

5 [image of cube train]

5, [ 6 ], [ 7 ], [ 8 ], [ 9 ]

4 + 5 = [ 9 ]

**b** [ 8 ] [image of cube train]

[ 2 ] [image of cube train]

[ 8 ], [ 9 ], [ 10 ]

[ 8 ] + [ 2 ] = [ 10 ]

29

# Teaching sequence

**2**

- Ask pupils to look at the pictures in the textbook. Use the cups and marbles to show them how to count on to answer the questions.
- Remind pupils to start counting from the greater number, even if given a smaller number first.

**3**

- Explain the 'counting on' strategy using cubes.
- Ask pupils to work in groups. Ask each group to make a 5-cube train and then add on 4 more cubes to find the answer to 4 + 5. Encourage pupils to use the 'counting on' strategy to find the answer.
- Ask the groups to make number trains to solve the other addition questions.

## What you will need

20 cubes in 2 colours (10 of each colour) for each group

## Additional activity

Encourage pupils to think of different ways to use the term 'more than' to describe two numbers.

E.g. 3 is more than 2.

3 is 1 more than 2.

## Teaching sequence

- Ask pupils to work in groups to make a 7-cube train. Encourage pupils to use the 'counting on' strategy to solve 7 + 2.
- Start with 7 cubes of the same colour. Fix 2 cubes of a different colour to the 7 cubes to make 9 cubes.
- Use the term 'more than' to show that 2 added on to 7 is 9. Say: "2 more than 7 is 9."

- Ask pupils to demonstrate the 'add on' concept using cubes.
- Encourage pupils to build a 5-cube train and add on 3 more cubes.
Say: "8 is 3 more than 5."

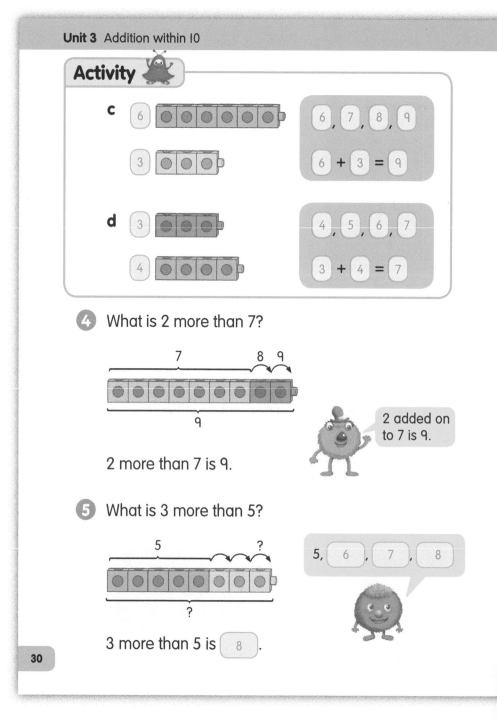

## Objective of activity
To reinforce the 'counting on' strategy

## Independent work
Practice I in Practice Book IA, pp 41 to 44.

## What you will need
2 packs of cards for each group:
7 cards with numbers 0 to 3
7 cards with numbers I to 7
(see Photocopy master 6 on page 260)

---

## Game

**6  Card fun!**

Players: 3
You will need:
• Two sets of number cards

How to play:

I  Make two sets of cards.

Set A  | 1 | 2 | 3 | 0 |
| 1 | 2 | 3 |

Set B  | 1 | 2 | 3 | 4 | 5 |
| 6 | 7 |

2  Player I picks a card from Set A.

3  Player 2 picks a card from Set B.

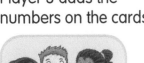

4  Player 3 adds the numbers on the cards.

5  Players I and 2 check the answer.

5 + 3 = 8   Correct!

6  Players get one point for each correct answer. Take turns to pick cards and add the numbers.

Play six rounds. The player with the most points wins.

Practice Book IA, p.41

31

## Teaching sequence

**6** *Game*

• Ask pupils to work in groups. Distribute the two packs of cards and model how to play the game. Guide pupils to follow the instructions in the textbook.

• Encourage pupils to use the 'counting on' strategy to find the answer.

• Look for pupils using the 'counting on' strategy to play the game.

## Additional activity

Ask pupils to work in pairs to think of two sets of objects: the total should be a maximum of 10 objects. Ask pupils to take turns to tell their partner about the two sets of objects. Their partner should then draw a corresponding number bond.

## Teaching sequence

- Explain the 'part-whole' concept using two groups of penguins.
- Ask pupils to use number bonds to find the total number of penguins from the two given groups.

- Ask pupils to look at the picture showing the toys.
- Ask pupils to describe the picture with reference to the different groups of toys.
- Ask pupils to complete the number bond based on the picture and write down the answer.

### Adding with number bonds

Number bonds can help you add.

How many penguins are there altogether?

$3 + 5 = ?$

$3 + 5 = 8$

How many toys are there altogether?

$2 + 6 = \boxed{8}$

32

**Independent work**

Practice 2 in Practice Book IA, pp 45 to 50.

**9** How many sheep are there altogether?

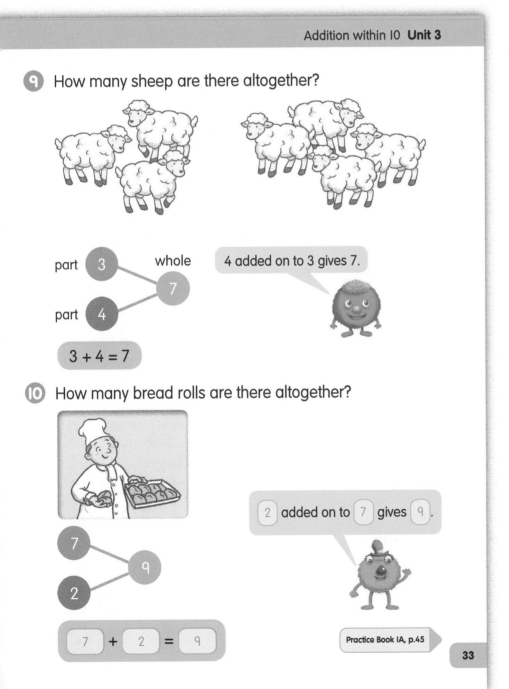

part 3

whole

7

part 4

4 added on to 3 gives 7.

3 + 4 = 7

**10** How many bread rolls are there altogether?

7

9

2

2 added on to 7 gives 9 .

7 + 2 = 9

Practice Book IA, p.45

33

## Teaching sequence

**9**

- Explain the 'adding on' concept using two groups of sheep.
- Emphasise that there are two groups of sheep; one group is joining the other group.
- Encourage pupils to use the number bond to help them find the total number of sheep from the two given groups.

**10**

- Ask pupils to look at the picture.
- Ask pupils to describe the two groups of bread rolls. Look for pupils who notice that one group is in the tray and that the baker adds the second group (from his hand) to the first group in the tray.
- Ask pupils to record their answers by recalling the relevant number bond.

## Learning objective:
## Making addition stories

**Pupils will be able to:**

- make addition stories based on pictures and various situations

## Key concept

Addition is associated with the 'part-whole' and 'adding on' concepts.

## What you will need

20 cubes in 2 colours (10 of each colour)

## Additional activity

Use a number balance to guide pupils through solving addition word problems.

## Teaching sequence

- Ask pupils to look at the picture in the textbook. Tell a story about the ducks in the picture. Use cubes to represent the ducks and write the addition sentence on the board.
- Emphasise the statements used in storytelling, and relate them to the concepts learnt such as 'adding on' and 'part-whole'.

---

### Let's Learn!

**Making up addition stories**

There are 5 ducks in a pond.
4 ducks get into the pond.
There are 9 ducks altogether.

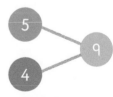

5 + 4 = 9

**Independent work**

Practice 3 in Practice Book IA, pp 51 to 54.

**Additional activity**

Ask pupils to make up addition stories using the 'part-whole' or 'adding on' concept.

---

Addition within 10 **Unit 3**

**2** Look at the pictures.
Make up addition stories.

**a**

2 big teddy bears          5 small teddy bears

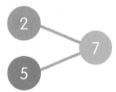   $2 + 5 = 7$

There are ⬚7⬚ teddy bears altogether.

**b**

 $3 + 1 = 4$

 Ask your child to make up addition stories about everyday situations around the home. For example, "There are 2 apples and 5 oranges. There are 7 pieces of fruit altogether."

Practice Book IA, p.51

35

**Teaching sequence**

**2**

**a**

- Ask pupils to look at the picture. Encourage them to tell a story. Summarise their story by emphasising the 'part-whole' concept in addition.
- Encourage pupils to relate the storytelling using groups to the number bonds.

**b**

- Ask pupils to look at the picture. Encourage them to tell a story. Summarise their story by emphasising the 'adding on' concept in addition.
- Encourage pupils to relate the storytelling using groups to the number bonds.

## Learning objectives:
## Solving word problems
**Pupils will be able to:**

- add by recognising two addition concepts: 'part-whole' and 'adding on'
- solve addition word problems using number bonds or the 'counting on' strategy

## Key concept

Applying the 'part-whole' and 'adding on' concepts in addition

## Teaching sequence

- Ask pupils to look at the picture. Work through the examples in the textbook together. Emphasise that the 'part-whole' concept is used here.

- Assess pupils' understanding by asking them to solve the word problem using the two strategies. Ask pupils to discuss the strategies they use.

---

**Unit 3** Addition within 10

**Let's Learn!**

### Solving word problems

6 girls are playing football.
3 boys are playing football with them.
How many children are playing football altogether?

$$6 + 3 = 9$$

9 children are playing football altogether.

② Millie has 3 red flowers.
She has 4 purple flowers.
How many flowers does Millie have altogether?

$$3 + 4 = 7$$

Millie has ⟨7⟩ flowers altogether.

36

## Thinking skills

- Analysing parts and whole
- Adding on

## Independent work

Practice 4 in Practice Book IA, pp 55 to 56.

**3** Peter makes 4 cakes.
He makes 5 more cakes.

How many cakes does Peter make altogether?

$4 + 5 = 9$

Peter makes 9 cakes altogether.

**4**

Ruby has no apples on her plate.
Tai puts 5 apples on Ruby's plate.
How many apples does Ruby have now?

$0 + 5 = 5$

Ruby has [ 5 ] apples now.

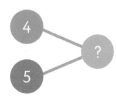

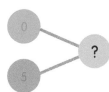

Practice Book IA, p.55

37

## Teaching sequence

**3** and **4**

- Ask pupils to work in groups to solve the word problems. They can use any strategy that they are comfortable with.
- Ask each group to present their strategies and answers to the class.
- Summarise the use of the 'part-whole' and 'adding on' strategies at the end of the lesson.

## Objective of activity

Pupils will be able to recall number bonds to solve the problem.

## Thinking skills

- Deduction
- Analysing parts and whole

## Heuristics for problem solving

- Using a diagram
- Guess and check

## What you will need

Photocopy master 7 (see page 261)

## Independent work

*Challenging Practice* and *Problem Solving* in Practice Book IA, pp 57 to 60.

## Teaching sequence

5 *Put On Your Thinking Caps!*

- Ask pupils to complete the activity in an exercise book.
- Encourage pupils to write out the question as an addition sentence, substituting the empty boxes from the textbook page with the numbers from the list.
- Look for pupils who are able to recall number bonds to solve the problem.
- Encourage pupils to use the 'guess and check' strategy. Ask pupils to guess 3 numbers that could form one of the addition sentences. Ask them to add 2 of the numbers and check if the sum equals the third number. If it does not, they should guess another 3 numbers and check again.

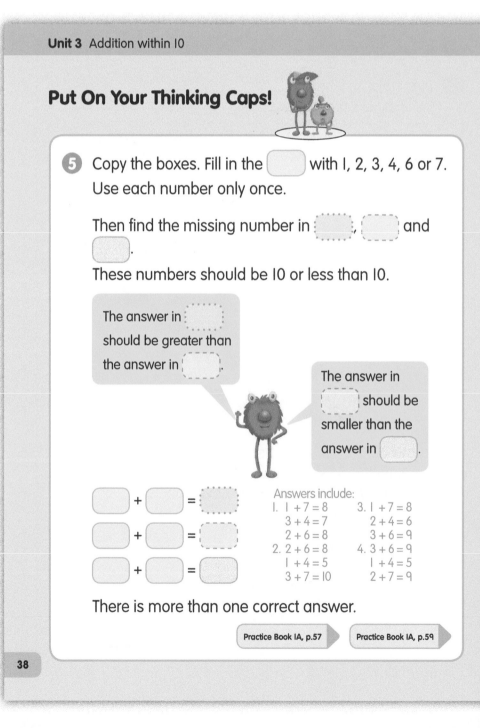

Unit 3 Addition within 10

## Put On Your Thinking Caps!

5 Copy the boxes. Fill in the ⬜ with I, 2, 3, 4, 6 or 7. Use each number only once.

Then find the missing number in ⬜, ⬜ and ⬜.

These numbers should be I0 or less than I0.

The answer in ⬜ should be greater than the answer in ⬜.

The answer in ⬜ should be smaller than the answer in ⬜.

⬜ + ⬜ = ⬜

⬜ + ⬜ = ⬜

⬜ + ⬜ = ⬜

Answers include:

| | |
|---|---|
| I. I + 7 = 8 | 3. I + 7 = 8 |
| 3 + 4 = 7 | 2 + 4 = 6 |
| 2 + 6 = 8 | 3 + 6 = 9 |
| 2. 2 + 6 = 8 | 4. 3 + 6 = 9 |
| I + 4 = 5 | I + 4 = 5 |
| 3 + 7 = I0 | 2 + 7 = 9 |

There is more than one correct answer.

Practice Book IA, p.57      Practice Book IA, p.59

38

# Unit 3 Addition within 10

Date: _____

## Practice 1   Ways to add

1 Count on. Fill in the spaces.

a

$4 + \underline{\ 3\ } = \underline{\ 7\ }$

b

$6 + \underline{\ 2\ } = \underline{\ 8\ }$

c

$5 + \underline{\ 3\ } = \underline{\ 8\ }$

d

$7 + \underline{\ 3\ } = \underline{\ 10\ }$

e

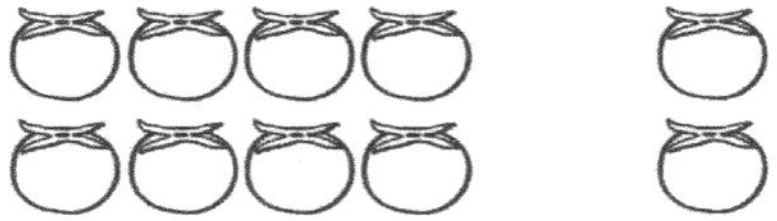

$8 + \underline{\ 2\ } = \underline{\ 10\ }$

**2** Add by counting on from the greater number.

Example
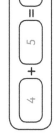
$\_\_\_ + 3 = 4$

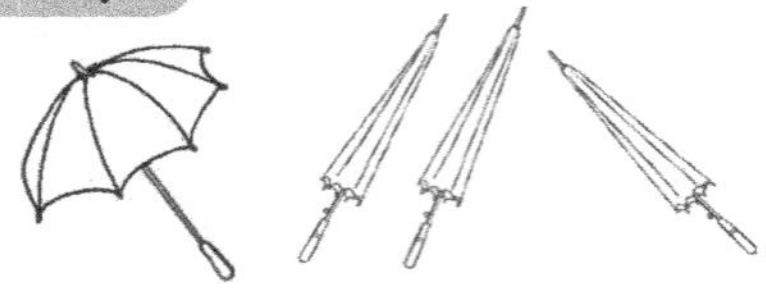

a   $4 + 4 = 8$

b  $3 + 7 = 10$

c  $2 + 3 = 5$

d  $9 + 1 = 10$

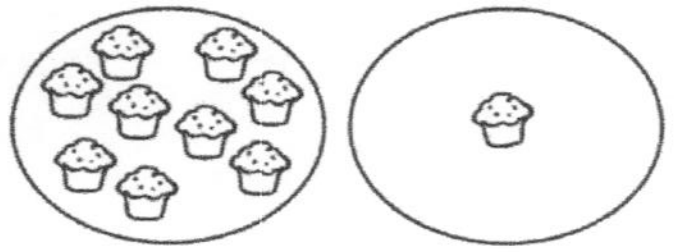

**3** Look at the dominoes and fill in the spaces.
Count on to find the answers.

a  $6 + 1 = 7$

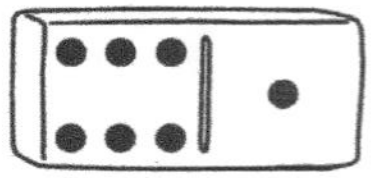

b  $4 + 5 = 9$

c  $5 + 1 = 6$

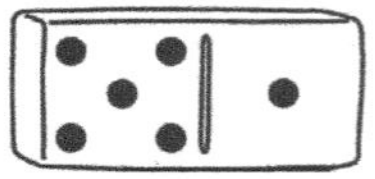

d  $6 + 3 = 9$

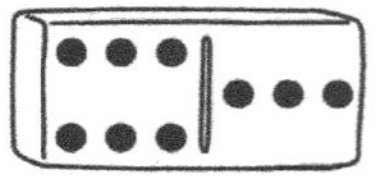

**4** Add by counting on from the greater number.

a  $4 + 1 = 5$   b  $6 + 2 = 8$

c  $9 + 1 = 10$   d  $3 + 4 = 7$

e  $2 + 7 = 9$   f  $5 + 5 = 10$

## Practice 2 | Ways to add

1. Complete the number bonds to show the parts and whole. Fill in the spaces.

**Example**

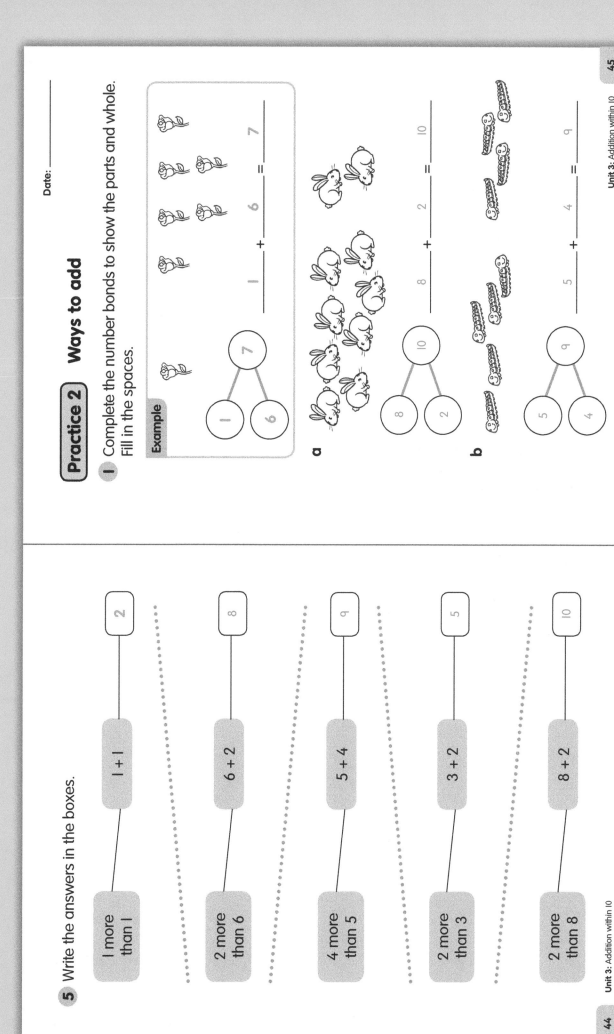

7 — 1 and 6

$1 + 6 = 7$

**a**

10 — 8 and 2

$8 + 2 = 10$

**b**

9 — 5 and 4

$5 + 4 = 9$

---

5. Write the answers in the boxes.

$1 + 1$ → 2 — 1 more than 1

$6 + 2$ → 8 — 2 more than 6

$5 + 4$ → 9 — 4 more than 5

$3 + 2$ → 5 — 2 more than 3

$8 + 2$ → 10 — 2 more than 8

**2** Complete the number bonds.
Fill in the spaces.

**a**

(1)(4) / (5)

$1 + 4 = 5$

**b**

(2)(6) / (8)

$2 + 6 = 8$

**c**

(5)(3) / (8)

$3 + 5 = 8$

**d**

(3)(3) / (6)

$3 + 3 = 6$

**e**

(2)(8) / (10)

$8 + 2 = 10$

**f**

(7)(2) / (9)

$2 + 7 = 9$

**c**

(9) / (3)(6)

$3 + 6 = 9$

**d**

(6) / (2)(4)

$2 + 4 = 6$

**e**

(10) / (5)(5)

$5 + 5 = 10$

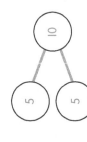

**4** Add the numbers.

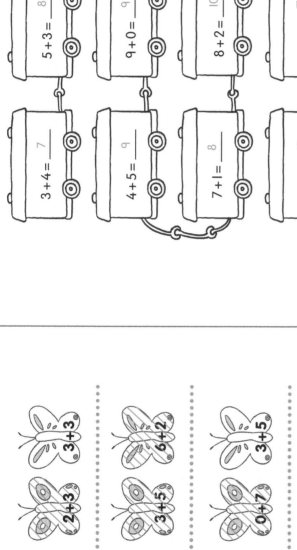

$5 + 3 = 8$

$9 + 0 = 9$

$8 + 2 = 10$

$2 + 5 = 7$

$3 + 4 = 7$

$4 + 5 = 9$

$7 + 1 = 8$

$6 + 4 = 10$

Colour this coach blue.

Colour the coaches and fill in the table.

| Answer | Colour | Number of coaches |
| --- | --- | --- |
| 7 | blue | 2 |
| 8 | green | 2 |
| 9 | orange | 2 |
| 10 | red | 2 |

**3** Colour the small butterflies that match the numbers on the big butterflies.

a   5   $1+4$   $2+3$   $3+3$

b   8   $2+7$   $3+5$   $6+2$

c   7   $6+1$   $0+7$   $3+5$

d   6   $2+4$   $3+2$   $5+1$

e   9   $2+6$   $1+8$   $4+5$

## Practice 3  Making up addition stories

1 Write addition stories. Fill in the boxes.

**Example**

__4__ children are playing.

__2__ children join them.

[4] + [2] = [6]

There are __6__ children altogether.

a

white cats          grey cats

There are __5__ white cats.

There are __3__ grey cats.

[5] + [3] = [8]

There are __8__ cats altogether.

5 A ball falls into the number machine.
Which ball is it?
Write the correct number on the ball.

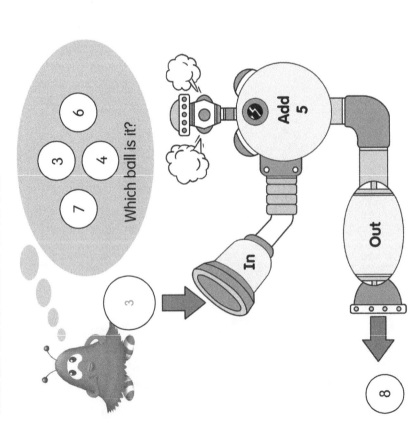

Which ball is it?

In  3    Add 5    Out  8

**b**

dogs playing

dogs sleeping

6 dogs are playing.

4 dogs are sleeping.

| 6 | + | 4 | = | 10 |

There are 10 dogs altogether.

**c**

heart stickers

star stickers

Miya has 2 heart stickers.

She buys 2 star stickers.

| 2 | + | 2 | = | 4 |

Miya has 4 stickers altogether.

**d**

7 girls are taking part in a race.

3 boys join in.

| 7 | + | 3 | = | 10 |

10 children are taking part in the race altogether.

**e**

Farha has 2 big fish.

She has 3 small fish.

| 2 | + | 3 | = | 5 |

Farha has 5 fish altogether.

## Practice 4 Solving word problems

1 Solve these word problems.

**Example**

__2__ children are reading.

__1__ child joins them.

How many children are reading now?

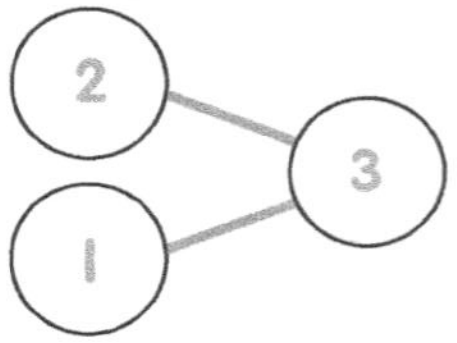

 $2 + 1 = 3$

__3__ children are reading now.

a

There are __4__ flags.

Tai comes along with __4__ flags.

How many flags are there altogether?

 4 + 4 = 8

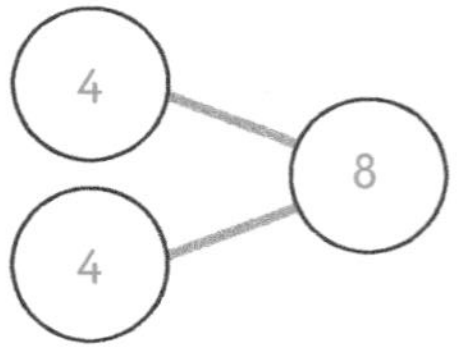

There are __8__ flags altogether.

---

2 Write your own addition story.
Use the words below to help.

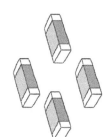

| rubbers | buys | new rubbers | altogether |

Answers vary. Example:

Ben has 4 rubbers.

He buys 5 new rubbers.

4 + 5 = 9

He has 9 rubbers altogether.

## Challenging Practice

1 Add the numbers.
Write the letters in the correct ⬡ to find the answer to this joke.

**What is a frog's favourite sweet?**

a 8 + 0 = __8__   L

b 0 + 0 = __0__   H   L

c 4 + 4 = __8__   P   O

d 3 + 2 = __5__   I

e 2 + 5 = __7__

f 7 + 2 = __9__

g 4 + 3 = __7__   O

h 6 + 2 = __8__   L

| L | O | L | L | I |   | H | O | P |
|---|---|---|---|---|---|---|---|---|
| 8 | 7 | 8 | 8 | 9 | - | 0 | 7 | 5 |

A

---

b There are __4__ footballs in a bag.
There are __3__ footballs on the grass.

How many footballs are there altogether?

There are __7__ footballs altogether.

$$4 + 3 = 7$$

c There are __7__ carrots on the plate.
Hardeep puts __1__ more carrot on the plate.

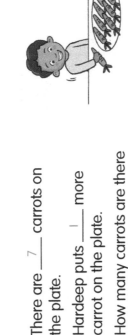

How many carrots are there altogether?

There are __8__ carrots altogether.

$$7 + 1 = 8$$

d Ella has __8__ pencils.
Jack gives her __2__ more.
How many pencils does Ella have now?

Now Ella has __10__ pencils.

$$8 + 2 = 10$$

## Problem Solving

**1** Write the numbers 5, 6, 8 and 9 in the □ and △.

The number in one □ is greater or smaller than the number in the other □ by 3.

The number in one △ is greater or smaller than the number in the other △ by 3.

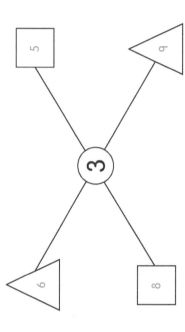

---

**2** Fill in the spaces.

a   $0 + \underline{6} = 6$    b   $3 + \underline{6} = 9$

c   $\underline{1} + 2 = 3$

d   $10 + \underline{0} = 10$

e   $7 + \underline{0} = 7$

f   $\underline{1} + 5 = 6$

g   $\underline{7} + 3 = 10$

**3** Ella and Farha have 10 presents altogether. They do not have the same number of presents. How many presents can Farha have?

Ella    Farha

You can give more than one answer.

Farha can have _____ presents.

Answers can be 1, 2, 3, 4, 6, 7, 8 or 9.

**2** Miya has some number candles.
Help her choose the correct number candle for her friend's birthday.

- Cross out two numbers that add up to 5.
- Cross out two numbers that add up to 10.
- Cross out the smaller number.

 5 6

7

The correct number candle is _____7_____.

Unit 3: Addition within 10

# Unit 4: Subtraction within 10

| Week | Learning Objectives | Thinking Skills | Resources |
|------|---------------------|-----------------|-----------|
| 6 | **(1) Ways to subtract**<br><br>Pupils will be able to:<br>• use the 'taking away' concept to subtract<br>• use the 'counting on' strategy to subtract<br>• use the 'counting back' strategy to subtract<br>• relate subtraction to number bonds<br>• subtract using number bonds | • Analysing parts and whole | • Pupil Textbook IA, pp 39 to 45<br>• Practice Book IA, pp 61 to 72<br>• Teacher's Guide IA, pp 73 to 79 |
| 6 | **(2) Making subtraction stories**<br><br>Pupils will be able to make subtraction stories based on pictures and various situations. | • Analysing parts and whole | • Pupil Textbook IA, pp 46 to 47<br>• Practice Book IA, pp 73 to 76<br>• Teacher's Guide IA, pp 80 to 81 |

# Unit 4: Subtraction within 10

| Week | Learning Objectives | Thinking Skills | Resources |
|------|---------------------|-----------------|-----------|
| 7 | **(3) Solving word problems**<br><br>Pupils will be able to:<br>• subtract by recognising two subtraction concepts: 'part-whole' and 'taking away'<br>• solve subtraction word problems using various strategies | • Analysing parts and whole | • Pupil Textbook IA, pp 48 to 49<br>• Practice Book IA, pp 77 to 78<br>• Teacher's Guide IA, pp 82 to 83 |
| 7 | **(4) Making a family of number sentences**<br><br>Pupils will be able to write a family of two addition and two subtraction number sentences, given a set of three related numbers.<br><br>*Let's Explore!*<br><br>Pupils will be able to apply number bonds to make addition and subtraction sentences in various ways, given a set of numbers. | • Identifying relationships<br>• Analysing parts and whole<br>• Induction | • Pupil Textbook IA, pp 50 to 52<br>• Practice Book IA, pp 79 to 80<br>• Teacher's Guide IA, pp 84 to 86 |

# Unit 4: Subtraction within 10

| Week | Learning Objectives | Thinking Skills | Resources |
|------|---------------------|-----------------|-----------|
| 7 | *Put On Your Thinking Caps!*<br><br>Pupils will be able to analyse numbers and form number bonds to solve problems. | • Analysing parts and whole<br>• Induction<br><br>Heuristic for problem solving:<br>• Solving part of the problem | • Pupil Textbook IA, pp 52 to 53<br>• Practice Book IA pp 8I to 84<br>• Teacher's Guide IA, pp 86 to 87 |
| | Review 2 | | • Practice Book IA, pp 85 to 88 |

## Summative assessment opportunities

Assessment Book I, Test 2, pp 9 to I4
For extension, Assessment Book I, Challenging Problems I, pp I5 to I6
Assessment Book I, Check-up I, pp I7 to 29

# Subtraction within 10

## Learning objectives:
## Ways to subtract

**Pupils will be able to:**

- use the 'taking away' concept to subtract
- use the 'counting on' strategy to subtract
- use the 'counting back' strategy to subtract
- relate subtraction to number bonds
- subtract using number bonds

## Key concept

Subtracting is associated with the 'part-whole' and 'taking away' concepts.

## What you will need

10 counters such as cubes

---

### Unit 4 Subtraction within 10

Let's Learn!

**Ways to subtract**

#### Subtracting by taking away

1. There are 9 spiders. Cross out 6 spiders.

Crossing out 6 spiders means you are taking away 6 spiders.

3 spiders are left.

$9 - 6 = 3$

whole   part   part

– is called **minus**. It means **subtract**.

$9 - 6 = 3$ is a **subtraction sentence**.
It says **nine minus six equals three**.

39

---

## Teaching sequence

**1**

- Start by using 9 cubes to represent the spiders in the picture. Take away 6 cubes and count the number of cubes left. Write the subtraction sentence on the board and explain the symbols used.
- Explain to pupils that the group of items taken away is one part or group, and the group of items remaining is another part or group. The total number of items is made up of these two parts: the part taken away, and the part remaining.
- The sentence involving the total and the two parts is the subtraction sentence.

**Thinking skill**
Analysing parts and whole

**What you will need**
20 cubes in 2 colours
(10 of each colour)

**Additional activity**
Ask pupils to think of different
ways to use the term 'less than'
to describe numbers.
E.g.  2 is 3 less than 5.
    3 less than 5 is 2.

**Teaching sequence**

- Use the problem to check if
  pupils relate the 'part-whole'
  concept to the 'taking away'
  concept.
- Encourage pupils to recognise
  which are the two parts and
  which is the whole.

- Introduce the 'less than'
  concept in subtraction, using
  cubes.
- Start with 6 cubes and then
  take away 2 to get 4. Explain
  that 2 less than 6 is 4.

- To solve this problem, start
  with 8 cubes and then take
  away 5 to get 3. Explain that
  5 less than 8 is 3.

---

**Unit 4** Subtraction within 10

2 Look at the pictures.
  Find the missing numbers.

  **a**
  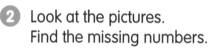

  $8 - 3 = \boxed{5}$

  **b**

  $10 - \boxed{4} = \boxed{6}$

3 What is 2 less than 6?

  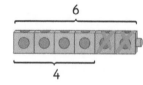

  $6 - 2 = 4$

  2 less than 6 is 4.

  2 taken away
  from 6 is 4.

4 What is 5 less than 8?

  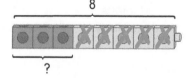

  $8 - 5 = \boxed{3}$

  5 less than 8 is $\boxed{3}$.

  40

---

## *Subtracting by counting on*

⑤ There are 9 flies.
6 flies are stuck in a web.
How many flies are still flying?

$9 - 6 = ?$
Count on from the smaller number: 6.
Stop at 9.

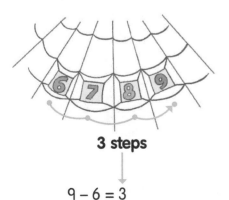

**3 steps**

$9 - 6 = 3$

6, 7, 8, 9

41

## Teaching sequence

⑤

Explain to pupils that there is
another way to subtract 6 from 9.
Show pupils how to start
counting on (forwards) from 6
until they reach 9. Say:
*"The number of steps taken is 3
so the answer is 3."*

## What you will need
10 cubes for each group

## Teaching sequence

**6** *Game*

- Model how to play the game.
- Ask pupils to work in groups. Ask each group to put a certain number of cubes on the table.
- Player 1 in each group then covers some of the cubes with their hands.
- Player 1 then asks the rest of the group to find out the number of cubes hidden.
- The rest of the group members should count the number of cubes that are not hidden, subtract them from the original number of cubes and say the number of cubes hidden.
- Player 1 reveals the cubes and the group members check their answer.
- Pupils take turns to be the player hiding the cubes.

## Game

**6** **What's hidden?**

Players: 3 to 4
You will need:
- 10 cubes

How to play:

**1** Player 1 chooses a number of  and shows them to the other players.

**2** Then player 1 hides some of the .

**3** The other players write the number of  player 1 hid by counting on.

There were 8. Now there are 5.

5, 6, 7, 8
You hid 3 !

**4** Player 1 checks their answers. Players get one point for each correct answer. Take turns to play.

Correct!

Play four rounds. The player with the most points wins.

42

## Teaching sequence

**7**

- Reinforce the 'counting on' strategy by asking pupils to use it to subtract.

**8**

- Explain to pupils that counting back is another way to do subtraction.
- Show pupils how to start by counting back from 9, using a number track if necessary. Say: "Count back 2 steps and the answer is 7."
- Emphasise to pupils that the number to be subtracted is the number of steps.

**9**

- Reinforce the 'counting back' strategy by asking pupils to use it to subtract.

---

Subtraction within I0  **Unit 4**

**7** Subtract the numbers. Count on from the smaller number.

**a** 8 − 6 = ☐ 2

**b** 6 − 3 = ☐ 3

**c** I0 − 7 = ☐ 3

**d** 9 − 5 = ☐ 4

### *Subtracting by counting back*

**8** 9 − 2 = ?
Start from the greater number, 9.
Count back 2 steps.

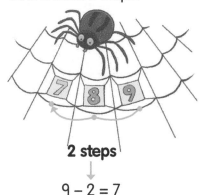

9, **8, 7**

**2 steps**
↓
9 − 2 = 7

**9** Subtract the numbers.
Count back from the greater number.

**a** 7 − 2 = ☐ 5

**b** 9 − 3 = ☐ 6

**c** 8 − 3 = ☐ 5

**d** I0 − 3 = ☐ 7

Home
Maths
Play Hit I! The first player begins with I0 and counts back up to 3 steps. The players take turns to count back. The player who says I wins.

Practice Book IA, p.6I

43

**Additional activity**

Ask pupils to work in pairs. One pupil draws a number bond and asks their partner to tell a simple subtraction story based on the number bond.

## Teaching sequence

- Ask pupils to look at the picture in the textbook and recall number bonds.
- Look for pupils who notice that there are two parts: the bean bags on the head and the bean bags on the floor. The total number is 9 and taking 4 away leaves 5.

**11**

- Ask pupils to look at the picture and recall number bonds.
- Look for pupils who notice that there are two parts: the green apples and the red apple. The total number is 10, and taking away 1 red apple leaves 9 green apples.

---

**Unit 4** Subtraction within 10

### *Subtracting with number bonds*

Number bonds can help you subtract.

 There are 9 bean bags altogether.
How many bean bags does Ruby have on her head?

$9 - 4 = ?$

part

whole

4

9

5

part

$9 - 4 = 5$

**11** There are 10 apples altogether.
How many are green?

$10 - 1 = ?$

part

whole

1

10

9

part

$10 - 1 = \boxed{9}$

44

## Independent work

Practice 2 in Practice Book IA,
pp 67 to 72.

**12** There are 6 sandwiches altogether.
How many are left on the plate?

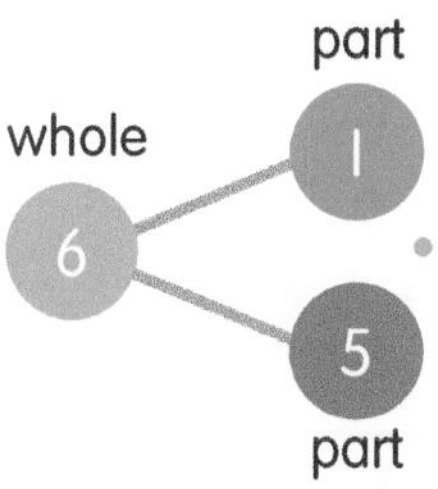

part

whole

6

1

5

part

$6 - 1 = 5$

**13** There are 10 cats altogether.
How many are not playing?

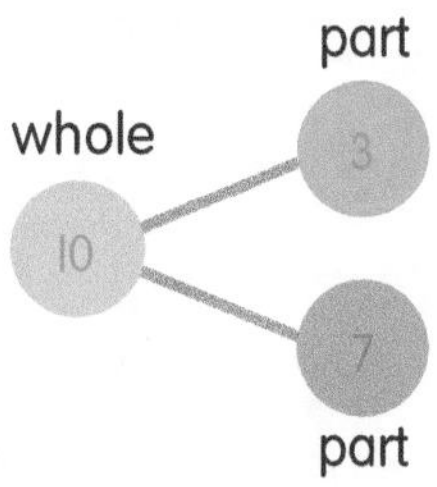

part

whole

10

3

7

part

 10 − 3 = 7

Practice Book IA, p.67

45

## Teaching sequence

**12**

- Ask pupils to look at the picture and recall number bonds.
- Look for pupils who notice that there are two parts: the sandwich being eaten and the sandwiches on the plate. The total number is 6, and taking 1 sandwich away leaves 5 sandwiches on the plate.

**13**

- Ask pupils to look at the picture and recall number bonds. Ask pupils to complete the question and discuss their answers with a partner.

## Learning objective: Making subtraction stories

**Pupils will be able to:**

- make subtraction stories based on pictures and various situations

## Key concept

Subtraction is associated with the 'part-whole' and 'taking away' concepts.

## What you will need

- 10 cubes (5 of each colour)
- Number balance
- 3 weights

## Teaching sequence

- Ask pupils to look at the picture in the textbook. Tell a story about the dogs and cats. Use cubes to represent the dogs and cats and write the addition sentence on the board. The story is about the total number of dogs and cats and the numbers of each.
- Emphasise the statements used in storytelling and relate to the concept being used such as the 'part-whole' concept in this story.
- Alternatively, use a number balance to guide pupils in subtraction.

- Ask pupils to look at the picture. Encourage them to tell a subtraction story.
- Summarise their story by emphasising the 'part-whole' concept in subtraction.
- Encourage them to relate the storytelling using groups and the number bonds.

---

**Unit 4** Subtraction within 10

**Let's Learn!**

### Making up subtraction stories

**1**

There are 7 animals.
4 are dogs.

7 − 4 = 3

3 are cats.

**2** Look at the picture.
Make up a subtraction story.

4 − 2 = 2

 **Home Maths** Encourage your child to make up subtraction stories about their favourite animals.

46

---

**Thinking skill**
Analysing parts and whole

**Independent work**
Practice 3 in Practice Book IA, pp 73 to 76.

## Teaching sequence

Subtraction within 10 **Unit 4**

Miya has 10 carrot sticks.
She gives Hardeep 2 carrot sticks.

10 – 2 = 8

Miya has 8 carrot sticks left.

**4** Look at the pictures.
Make up a subtraction story.

8 – 8 = 0

**3**

- Tell a story about Miya, Hardeep and the carrot sticks. Relate the story to the 'taking away' concept and number bonds.
- Look for pupils who notice that the number of carrot sticks taken away is one group and the remaining carrot sticks is another group.

**4**

- Ask pupils to look at the picture. Encourage them to tell a subtraction story.
- Summarise their story by emphasising the 'taking away' concept in the story.
- Encourage pupils to relate the storytelling using groups and the number bonds.
- Ask pupils to name the two groups in the number bond in relation to the story.

Home Maths — Ask your child to make up subtraction stories about everyday life at home. For example, "We have 8 plates in the cupboard. We use 4 plates for dinner. There are 4 plates left in the cupboard."

Practice Book IA, p.73

47

**Unit 4:** Subtraction within 10     81

## Solving word problems

**Pupils will be able to:**

- subtract by recognising two subtraction concepts: 'part-whole' and 'taking away'
- solve subtraction word problems using various strategies

## Key concept

Applying the 'part-whole' and 'taking away' concepts in subtraction.

## Teaching sequence

- Explain that the problem involves the 'part-whole' concept. In this case the parts are the marbles that Jack and Farha have. The total is 9: Jack has 7 marbles in his part and Farha's part is unknown.
- Explain that subtraction is used to find Farha's part.

- Look for pupils who can apply the 'taking away' concept to solve the problem.

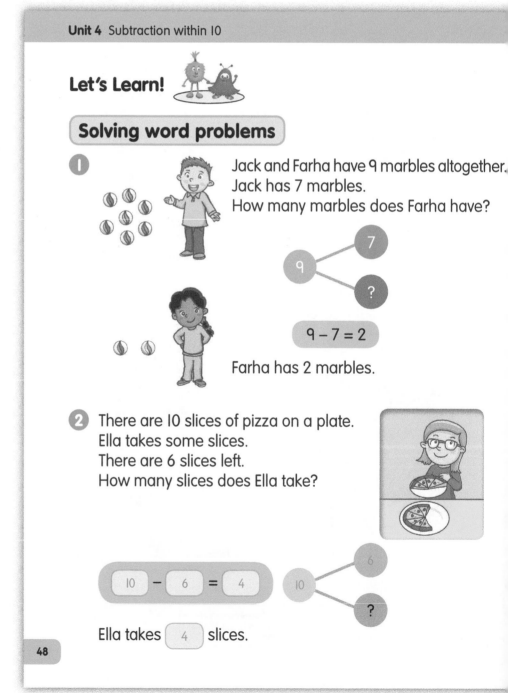

**Unit 4** Subtraction within 10

**Let's Learn!**

**Solving word problems**

1. Jack and Farha have 9 marbles altogether.
   Jack has 7 marbles.
   How many marbles does Farha have?

   $9 - 7 = 2$

   Farha has 2 marbles.

2. There are 10 slices of pizza on a plate.
   Ella takes some slices.
   There are 6 slices left.
   How many slices does Ella take?

   $10 - 6 = 4$

   Ella takes [ 4 ] slices.

48

## Thinking skill

Analysing parts and whole

## Independent work

Practice 4 in Practice Book IA,
pp 77 to 78.

## Additional activity

Ask pupils to work in pairs.
Ask one pair to tell a subtraction
story using the 'part-whole'
concept and their partner to tell
another story using the 'taking
away' concept.

## Teaching sequence

**3**

- Ask pupils to explain which is
  the whole and which are the
  two parts in the problem.
- Guide pupils to use
  subtraction to find the number
  of rabbits still sleeping.

**4**

- Look for pupils who can apply
  the 'taking away' concept to
  solve the problem.

**3**

There are 7 rabbits.
4 rabbits are playing.
The rest are sleeping.
How many rabbits are sleeping?

$7 - 4 = 3$

3 rabbits are sleeping.

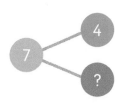

**4**

Tai has 9 balloons.
2 balloons pop.
How many balloons are left?

7 balloons are left.

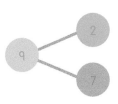

Practice Book IA, p.77

49

## Learning objective:
## Making a family of number sentences

**Pupils will be able to:**

- write a family of two addition and two subtraction number sentences, given a set of three related numbers

## Key concept

A family of number sentences can be written from a set of three related numbers.

## What you will need

5 yellow cubes and 2 blue cubes

## Teaching sequence

- Show pupils 5 yellow cubes and 2 blue cubes. Ask them to say or write four number sentences based on these cubes.
- Write the number sentences on the board. Point out that all the sentences revolve around the same three numbers in a number bond (5, 2, 7) and that they make up a family of number sentences.

---

**Unit 4** Subtraction within 10

## Let's Learn!

### Making a family of number sentences

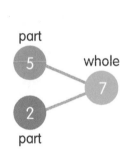

part

5

whole

7

2

part

How many balls of string are yellow?

$7 - 2 = 5$

How many balls of string are blue?

$7 - 5 = 2$

How many balls of string are there altogether?

$2 + 5 = 7$   or   $5 + 2 = 7$

. . . . . . . . . . . . . . . . . . . . . . . . . . .

$7 - 2 = 5$    $7 - 5 = 2$    $2 + 5 = 7$    $5 + 2 = 7$

These make a family of number sentences.

50

**Thinking skill**
Identifying relationships

**Independent work**
Practice 5 in Practice Book IA, pp 79 to 80.

**Teaching sequence**

**2**

- Encourage pupils to practise making a family of number sentences.
- Look for pupils who notice that there are four teddy bears with a red bow tie and two teddy bears with a blue bow tie, and write addition and subtraction sentences related to these teddy bears.

**3**

- Ask pupils to write their own number sentences for the pictures shown.

---

Subtraction within 10 **Unit 4**

**2** Look at the picture.
Make up a family of number sentences.

$$4 + 2 = 6$$

$$6 - 2 = 4$$

$$2 + 4 = 6$$

$$6 - 4 = 2$$

**3** Look at the pictures.
Make up a family of number sentences.

**a**

$$6 + 2 = 8$$
$$2 + 6 = 8$$
$$8 - 2 = 6$$
$$8 - 6 = 2$$

**b**

$$6 + 3 = 9$$
$$3 + 6 = 9$$
$$9 - 3 = 6$$
$$9 - 6 = 3$$

**Home Maths**
Put counters (or coloured pegs, or pieces of coloured paper) into 2 groups. Each group should have 2 colours and not more than 10 counters. Ask your child to look at the groups and make up two families of number sentences. Remember that the numbers should add up to 10 or less.

Practice Book IA, p.79    **51**

Unit 4: Subtraction within 10    **85**

## Objectives of activities

**Pupils will be able to:**
- apply number bonds to make addition and subtraction sentences in various ways, given a set of numbers.
- analyse numbers and form number bonds to solve problems.

## What you will need

Photocopy masters 8 and 9 (see pages 262 and 263)

## Thinking skills
- Identifying relationships
- Analysing parts and whole
- Induction

## Heuristic for problem solving

Solving part of the problem

## Teaching sequence

**4** *Let's Explore!*

- Encourage pupils to practise using number bonds to make addition and subtraction sentences in various ways given a set of numbers.

**5** *Put On Your Thinking Caps!*

**a**

- Pupils will need to use their knowledge of number bonds to 10 to solve this problem.
- Encourage pupils to start by first placing the largest number in the orange circle. Then finding the number bonds to 10 to complete the square.

---

**Unit 4** Subtraction within 10

### Let's Explore!

**4** You will need these cards.

| 2 | 3 | 6 | 8 | 9 | 10 | + | − | = |

Use the cards to make number sentences.
Write down all the number sentences you make.

$6 + 3 = 9$ $\quad 9 - 3 = 6$ $\quad 2 + 6 = 8$
$3 + 6 = 9$ $\quad 9 - 6 = 3$ $\quad 6 + 2 = 8$
$\qquad\qquad\qquad\qquad\qquad\quad 8 - 2 = 6$
$\qquad\qquad\qquad\qquad\qquad\quad 8 - 6 = 2$

$2 + 8 = 10$
$8 + 2 = 10$
$10 - 2 = 8$
$10 - 8 = 2$

### Put On Your Thinking Caps!

**5** **a** Use all these numbers to solve the puzzle. Use each number once.

$1 \quad 2 \quad 5 \quad 6 \quad 8 \quad 9 \quad 10$

➜ and ⬇ mean =.

(Hint: The number in the ⬭ is the greatest.)

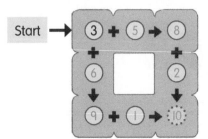

Start ➜ ③ **+** ⑤ ➜ ⑧
**+**            **+**
⑥              ②
⬇             ⬇
⑨ **+** ① ➜ ⑩

52

**Independent work**

*Challenging Practice, Problem Solving* and Review 2 in Practice Book IA, pp 81 to 88.

## Put On Your Thinking Caps!

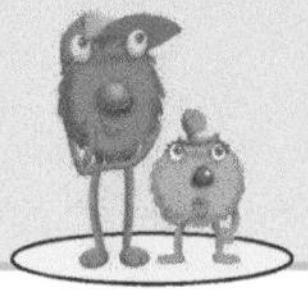

**b**  Use all these numbers to solve the puzzle.
Use each number once.

( 2 )( 3 )( 4 )( 5 )( 6 )( 7 )( 8 )

→ and ↓ mean =.

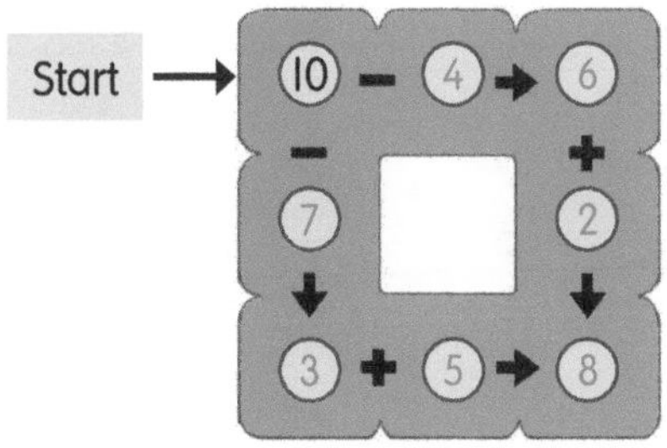

Start →  (10) – (4) → (6)
—
(7)          (2)
+
↓            ↓
(3) + (5) → (8)

Practice Book IA, p.81    Practice Book IA, p.84

53

**Teaching sequence**

**b**

- Remind pupils to use subtraction number bonds to solve the problem.
- Suggest to pupils that because 10 is the largest number, they need to subtract from the number 10.

# Unit 4

## Subtraction within 10

Date: _____

### Practice 1  Ways to subtract

1 Cross out the correct number of objects.
Circle the answer.

**Example**

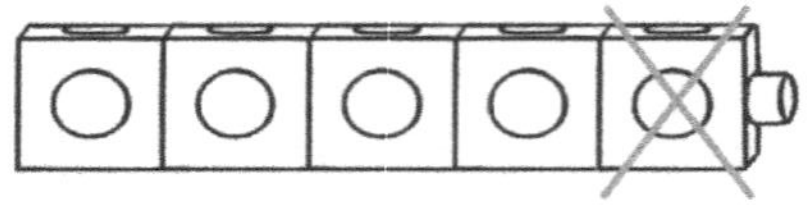

5 − 1 = ?

• • • • • • • •  3  (4)  5

a

10 − 1 = ?

• • • • • • • •  (9)  8  7

b

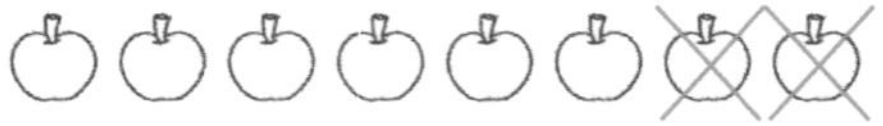

8 − 2 = ?

• • • • • • • •  2  (6)  8

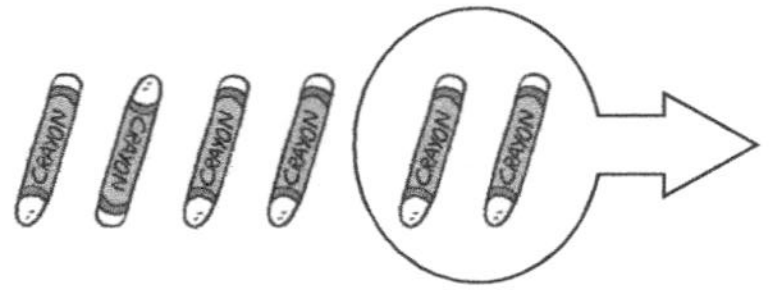

**3** Write the answers in the boxes.

| | 3 − 1 | 1 less<br>than 3 | 2 |
|---|---|---|---|

6 − 3 — 3 less than 6 — 3

10 − 5 — 5 less than 10 — 5

7 − 4 — 4 less than 7 — 3

9 − 2 — 2 less than 9 — 7

---

**2** Look at the pictures.
Complete the subtraction sentences.

**Example**

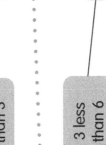 

9 − 1 = 8

**a** 5 − 3 = 2

**b** 9 − 3 = 6

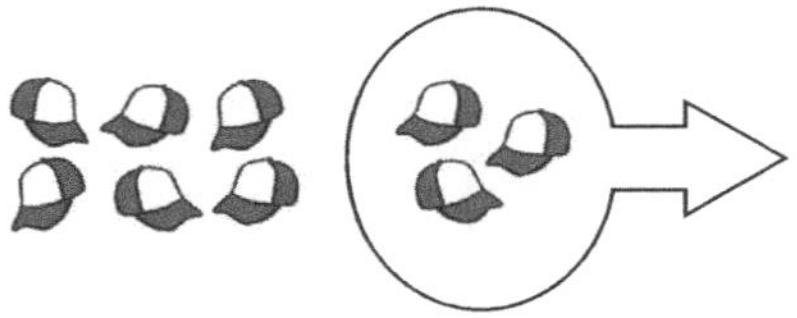

**c** 10 − 4 = 6

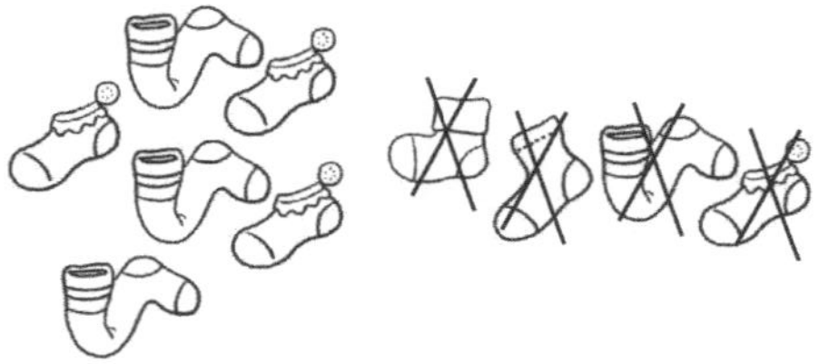

**d** 6 − 2 = 4

**4** Count on. Fill in the spaces.

Example

Start here

$5 - 2 = \underline{3}$

a   $7 - 4 = \underline{3}$

b   $5 - 3 = \underline{2}$

c   $9 - 5 = \underline{4}$

d   $8 - 4 = \underline{4}$

e   $7 - 6 = \underline{1}$

f   $10 - 8 = \underline{2}$

**5** Count back. Fill in the spaces.

Example

Start here

Count back

$9 - 4 = \underline{5}$

a   $10 - 1 = \underline{9}$

b   $8 - 2 = \underline{6}$

c   $7 - 3 = \underline{4}$

d   $5 - 4 = \underline{1}$

e   $8 - 5 = \underline{3}$

f   $6 - 4 = \underline{2}$

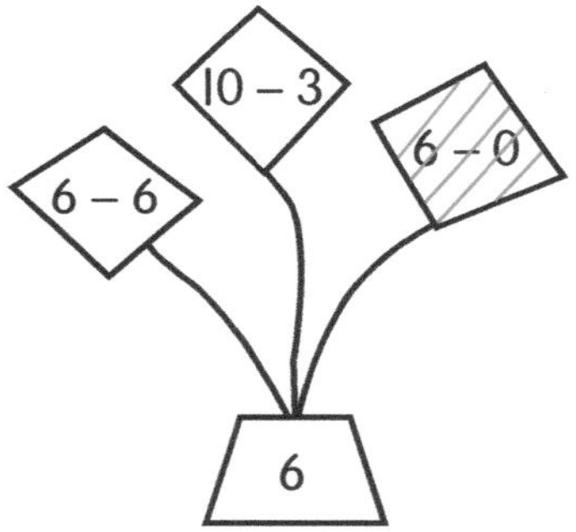

Date: _____

## Practice 2   Ways to subtract

1. Fill in the number bond.
   Complete the subtraction sentence.

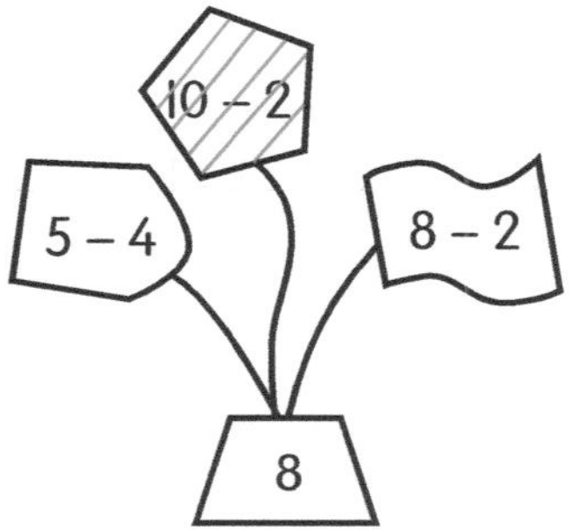

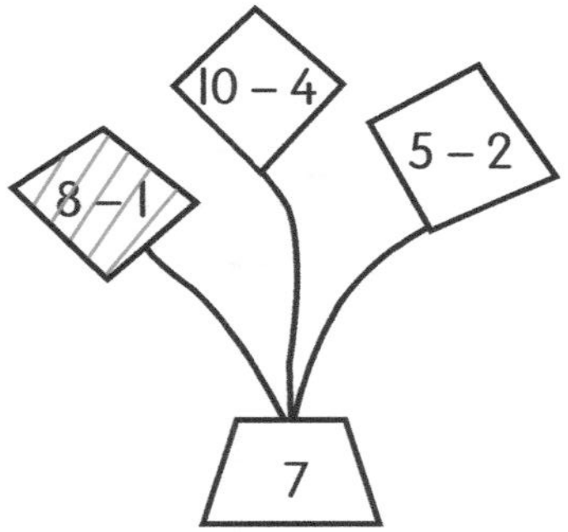

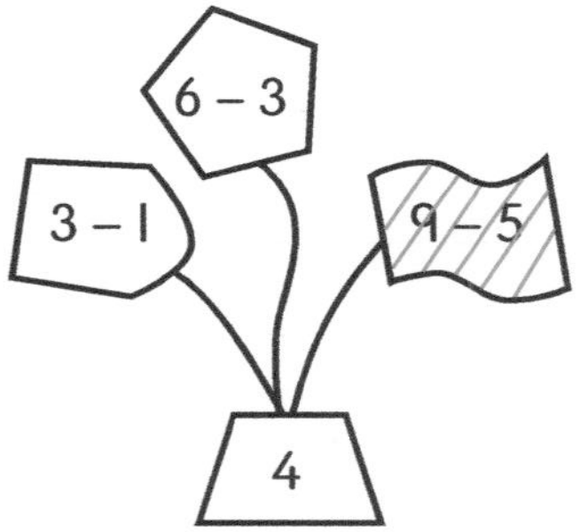

a)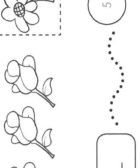

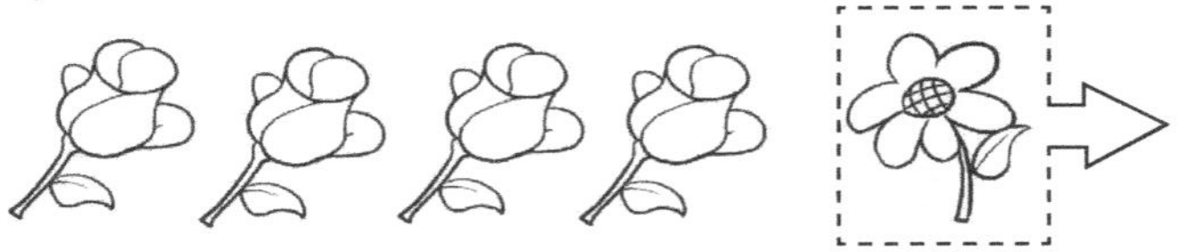

5 → 1, 4

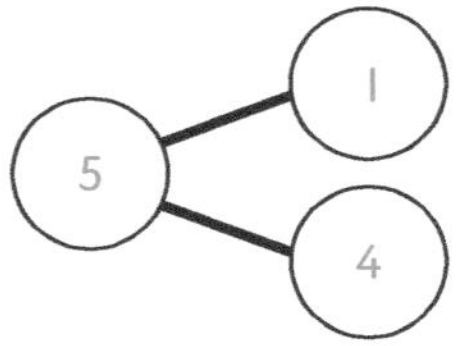

5 – 1 = __4__

b)

6 → 3, 3

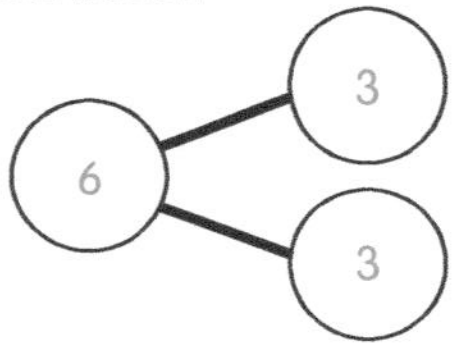

6 – 3 = __3__

c)

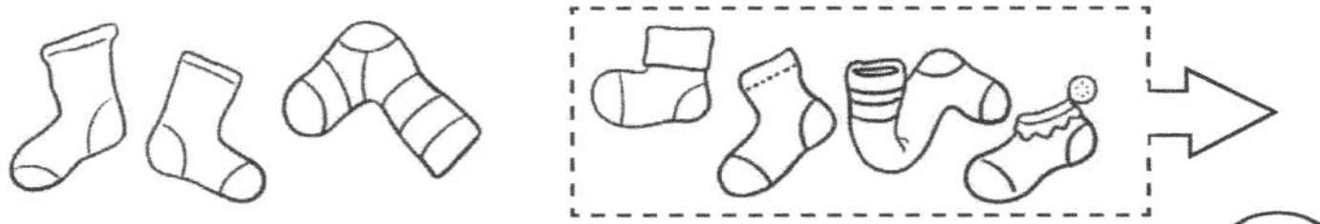

7 → 4, 3

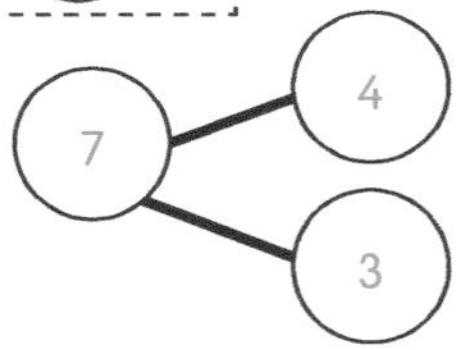

7 – 4 = __3__

---

6 Colour the correct label.

**Example**

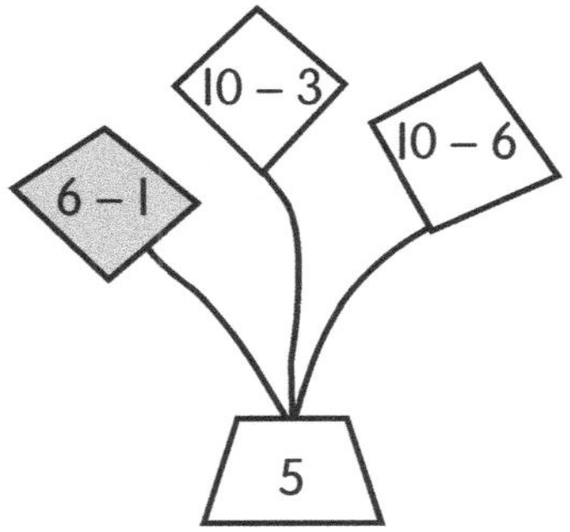

5 : 10 – 6 , 10 – 3 , **6 – 1**

a) 8 : **10 – 2** , 5 – 4 , 8 – 2

b) 7 : 10 – 4 , 5 – 2 , **8 – 1**

c) 4 : 6 – 3 , 3 – 1 , **9 – 5**

d) 6 : 10 – 3 , **6 – 0** , 6 – 6

**2** Complete the number bonds. Fill in the spaces.

**Example**

7 – 1 = [6]

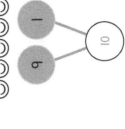

Number bond: 1, 7, 6

**a** 10 – 3 = [7]

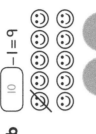

Number bond: 7, 3, 10

**b** 10 – 1 = 9

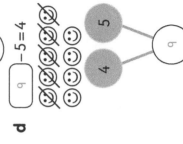

Number bond: 9, 1, 10

**c** 4 – 0 = 4

Number bond: 4, 0, 4

**d** 9 – 5 = 4

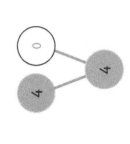

Number bond: 4, 5, 9

---

**d**

8 – 3 = [5]

Number bond: 8, 3, 5

**e**

9 – 3 = [6]

Number bond: 9, 3, 6

**f**

10 – 8 = [2]

Number bond: 10, 8, 2

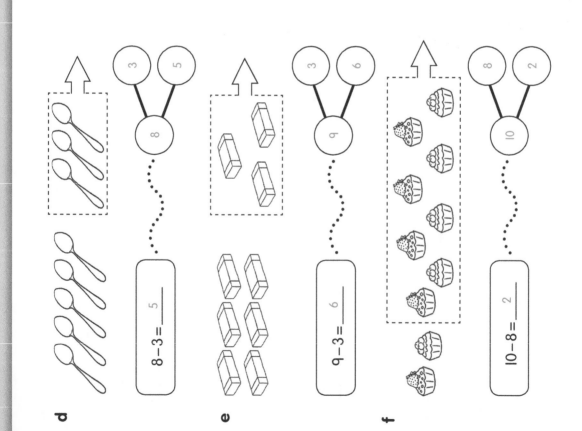

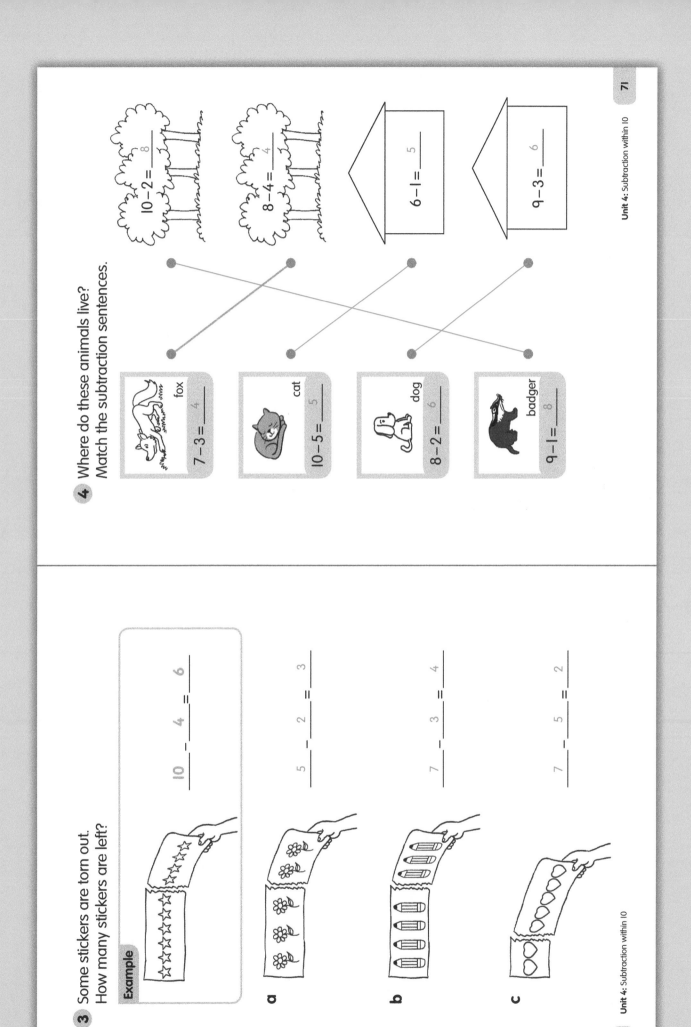

**4** Where do these animals live?
Match the subtraction sentences.

fox
7 – 3 = _4_

cat
10 – 5 = _5_

dog
8 – 2 = _6_

badger
9 – 1 = _8_

10 – 2 = _8_

8 – 4 = _4_

6 – 1 = _5_

9 – 3 = _6_

**3** Some stickers are torn out.
How many stickers are left?

**Example**

10 — — 4 = 6

**a**  5 — — 2 = 3

**b**  7 — — 3 = 4

**c**  7 — — 5 = 2

Date: _____

## Practice 3  Making up subtraction stories

1 Write subtraction stories. Fill in the spaces.

**Example**

There are __8__ pineapples.

Jack's dad takes __2__ pineapples away.

| 8 | – | 2 | = | 6 |

__6__ pineapples are left.

**a**

There are __9__ butterflies.

__3__ don't have a pattern on their wings.

| 9 | – | 3 | = | 6 |

__6__ butterflies have a pattern on their wings.

---

5 Subtract the numbers.

**a** 10 – 5 = __5__   **R**

**b** 9 – 8 = __1__   **I**

**c** 6 – 3 = __3__   **B**

**d** 7 – 5 = __2__   **S**

**e** 9 – 4 = __5__   **R**

**f** 10 – 0 = __10__  **A**

**g** 9 – 1 = __8__   **E**

**h** 6 – 2 = __4__   **V**

**i** 10 – 3 = __7__   **K**

**j** 9 – 0 = __9__   **N**

Write the letters in the correct ☐ to find the answer to this joke.

**Where do fish keep their money?**

| R | I | V | E | R | | B | A | N | K | S |
|---|---|---|---|---|---|---|---|---|---|---|
| In | | | | | | | | | | |
| 5 | 1 | 4 | 8 | 5 | | 3 | 10 | 9 | 7 | 2 |

**2** Write your own subtraction story. Use the words below to help.

**a**

| children | leaving | staying |

Answers vary. Example:

There are 7 children at a party.

3 children are leaving.

[ 7 ] ( − ) [ 3 ] ( = ) [ 4 ]

4 children are staying.

**b**

sitting        flying away

There are __8__ birds.

__5__ birds are sitting.

[ 8 ] ( − ) [ 5 ] ( = ) [ 3 ]

__3__ birds are flying away.

**c**

roses        tulips

There are __10__ flowers.

__5__ flowers are tulips.

[ 10 ] ( − ) [ 5 ] ( = ) [ 5 ]

__5__ flowers are roses.

## Practice 4  Solving word problems

1  Solve these word problems.

**Example**

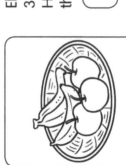

There are 5 children.
1 child walks off.
How many children are left?

$$5 - 1 = 4$$

There are ___4___ children left.

**a**

Ella has 6 pieces of fruit.
3 of them are apples.
How many bananas are there?

$$6 - 3 = 3$$

There are ___3___ bananas.

**b**

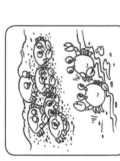

8 crabs are on the beach.
2 crabs crawl away.
How many crabs are left?

$$8 - 2 = 6$$

___6___ crabs are left.

---

**b**

| birds | in a tree | fly away | left |

Answers vary. Example

There are 6 birds.

4 birds fly away.

| 6 | − | 4 | = | 2 |

There are 2 birds left in a tree.

## Practice 5  Making a family of number sentences

1 Write a family of number sentences for each picture.

**Example**

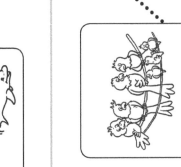

$1 + 2 = 3$
$2 + 1 = 3$
$3 - 1 = 2$
$3 - 2 = 1$

a
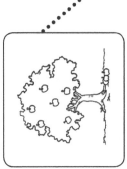

$3 + 4 = 7$
$4 + 3 = 7$
$7 - 3 = 4$
$7 - 4 = 3$

b

$6 + 3 = 9$
$3 + 6 = 9$
$9 - 3 = 6$
$9 - 6 = 3$

c

Tai has 9 toys.
6 of the toys are cars and the rest are bears.
How many bears does Tai have?

$9 - 6 = 3$

Tai has __3__ bears.

d

There are 10 eggs.
3 eggs are broken.
How many eggs are left?

$10 - 3 = 7$

__7__ eggs are left.

e

Miya blows 4 bubbles.
Then she pops all of them.
How many bubbles are left?

$4 - 4 = 0$

__0__ bubbles are left.

## Challenging Practice

1 Fill in the boxes.

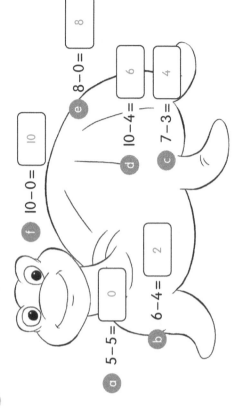

a  5 − 5 = 0
b  6 − 4 = 2
c  7 − 3 = 4
d  10 − 4 = 6
e  8 − 0 = 8
f  10 − 0 = 10

Now write your answers below.

| Dot | a | b | c | d | e | f |
| --- | --- | --- | --- | --- | --- | --- |
| Answer | 0 | 2 | 4 | 6 | 8 | 10 |

Fill in the boxes.

Answer f is 2 more than answer e .

Answer a is 2 less than answer b .

c

3 + 7 = 10
7 + 3 = 10
10 − 3 = 7
10 − 7 = 3

d
6 + 2 = 8
2 + 6 = 8
8 − 6 = 2
8 − 2 = 6

e
Answers vary. Examples:
8 + 2 = 10
2 + 8 = 10
10 − 8 = 2
10 − 2 = 8

6 + 2 = 8      6 + 4 = 10
2 + 6 = 8      4 + 6 = 10
8 − 6 = 2      10 − 6 = 4
8 − 2 = 6      10 − 4 = 6

**2** Complete the number bonds. Fill in the spaces.

a   7 − 2 = 5

7
5   2

b   6 − 5 = 1

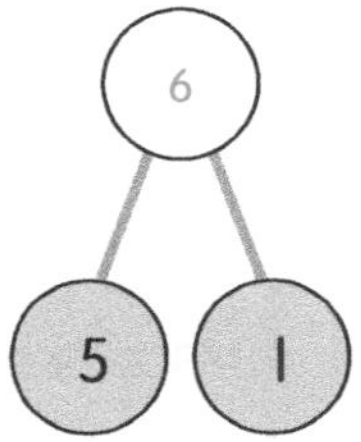

6
5   1

c   10 − 6 = 4

10
6   4

d   9 − 1 = 8

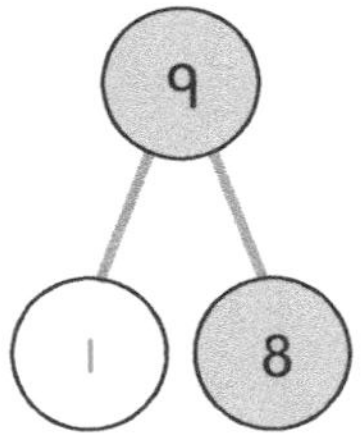

9
1   8

**3** Fill in the spaces.

a   7 − 3 = 4

b   5 − 4 = 1

c   10 − 8 = 2

d   9 − 6 = 3

e   6 − 6 = 0

f   8 − 6 = 2

g   10 − 9 = 1

h   8 − 4 = 4

---

**4** Pick 3 numbers from each set to make a family of number sentences.

a

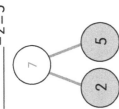

5   7   2
5   + 2 = 7
2   + 5 = 7
7   − 5 = 2
7   − 2 = 5

b

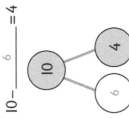

7   + 2 = 9
2   + 7 = 9
9   − 7 = 2
9   − 2 = 7

# Review 2

Date: _____

1 Add the numbers.

$2 + 8 = 10$

2 Complete the number bonds.
Fill in the spaces.

a $\underline{5} + 5 = 10$

(10, 5, 5 number bond)

b $8 - 3 = \underline{5}$

(8, 3, 5 number bond)

3 Fill in the spaces.

a 2 more than 6 is $\underline{8}$.

b 3 less than 7 is $\underline{4}$.

c $\underline{9}$ is 4 more than 5.

d $\underline{5}$ is 5 less than 10.

---

## Problem Solving

Date: _____

1 I think of two numbers.
When I add the numbers, the answer is 5.

$0 + 5 = 5$
$1 + 4 = 5$
$2 + 3 = 5$

When I subtract the numbers, the answer is 1.

Try! 
$5 - 0 = 5$ ✗
$4 - 1 = 3$ ✗
$3 - 2 = 1$ ✓

What are the two numbers?
The two numbers are 2 and 3.

Now try this.
I think of two numbers.
When I add the numbers, the answer is 8.
When I subtract the numbers, the answer is less than 6.
What are the two numbers?

More than one answer is possible.

The two numbers are

___Answers vary___ and ___Answers vary___.

**7** There are 6 white rabbits and 2 grey rabbits.
How many rabbits are there altogether?

$6 + 2 = 8$

There are ___8___ rabbits altogether.

**8** Ben has 10 candles on his cake.
He blows out 3 candles.
How many lit candles are left?

$10 - 3 = 7$

___7___ lit candles are left.

---

**4** Fill in the spaces.

**a** $2 + \underline{\;6\;} = 8$   **b** $\underline{\;4\;} + 5 = 9$

**c** $5 - \underline{\;4\;} = 1$   **d** $\underline{\;6\;} - 6 = 0$

**5** Pick three numbers from the set and make a family of number sentences.

5  4  1  2

$4 + 1 = 5$
$1 + 4 = 5$
$5 - 1 = 4$
$5 - 4 = 1$

**6** Millie has 3 pens in one hand.
She has 5 pens in the other hand.
How many pens does Millie have altogether?

$3 + 5 = 8$

Millie has ___8___ pens altogether.

**Answers Unit 4:** Subtraction within 10

**9** Hardeep has 9 buttons.
5 of the buttons are black and the rest are white.
How many white buttons does Hardeep have?

$9 - 5 = 4$

Hardeep has ___4___ white buttons.

**10** Miya lost 3 balloons.
She has 6 balloons left.
How many balloons did Miya have to begin with?

$3 + 6 = 9$

Miya had ___9___ balloons to begin with.

# Unit 5: Shapes and Patterns

## Medium-term plan

| Week | Learning Objectives | Thinking Skills | Resources |
|---|---|---|---|
| 8 | **(1) Getting to know shapes**<br><br>Pupils will be able to:<br>• look at a shape and identify it as a circle, triangle, square or rectangle<br>• classify and group the different shapes as circles, triangles, squares or rectangles<br>• describe the characteristics of the different shapes and also explain why they are not another shape | • Classifying | • Pupil Textbook 1A, pp 54 to 56<br>• Practice Book 1B, pp 5 to 8<br>• Teacher's Guide 1A, pp 106 to 108 |
| 8 | **(2) Making pictures from shapes**<br><br>Pupils will be able to:<br>• identify the four basic shapes and find the number of each shape in a given picture<br>• make pictures using the four basic shapes | | • Pupil Textbook 1A, pp 57 to 59<br>• Practice Book 1B, pp 9 to 14<br>• Teacher's Guide 1A, pp 109 to 111 |

# Unit 5: Shapes and Patterns

| Week | Learning Objectives | Thinking Skills | Resources |
|------|---------------------|-----------------|-----------|
| 8 | **(3) Seeing shapes in things around us**<br><br>Pupils will be able to:<br>• identify the four basic shapes in real-life objects<br>• name objects that have these basic shapes | • Classifying | • Pupil Textbook IA, pp 60 to 61<br>• Practice Book IB, pp 15 to 18<br>• Teacher's Guide IA, pp 112 to 113 |
| 9 | **(4) Getting to know patterns**<br><br>Pupils will be able to:<br>• identify and complete a pattern according to one or two attributes: shape, size or colour<br>• use shapes to make a pattern | • Identifying patterns | • Pupil Textbook IA, pp 62 to 63<br>• Practice Book IB, pp 19 to 24<br>• Teacher's Guide IA, pp 114 to 115 |

# Unit 5: Shapes and Patterns

# Medium-term plan

| Week | Learning Objectives | Thinking Skills | Resources |
|---|---|---|---|
| 9 | **(5) Making more patterns**<br><br>Pupils will be able to:<br>• identify the attributes of size, colour or object in a 3D pattern<br>• complete a pattern with 3D shapes consisting of cubes, cuboids, cones and cylinders | • Identifying patterns<br>• Sequencing<br>• Analysing and interpreting | • Pupil Textbook IA, pp 64 to 65<br>• Practice Book IB, pp 25 to 26<br>• Teacher's Guide IA, pp II6 to II7 |
| 9 | *Put On Your Thinking Caps!*<br><br>Pupils will be able to:<br>• classify shapes by colour and size<br>• recognise a pattern and identify the missing item | • Classifying<br>• Identifying patterns<br>• Analysing | • Pupil Textbook IA, p 66<br>• Practice Book IB, pp 27 to 32<br>• Teacher's Guide IA, p II8 |

# Shapes and Patterns

## Learning objectives: Getting to know shapes

**Pupils will be able to:**

- look at a shape and identify it as a circle, triangle, square or rectangle
- classify and group the different shapes as circles, triangles, squares or rectangles
- describe the characteristics of the different shapes and also explain why they are not another shape

## Key concepts

- A circle has no corners and no sides.
- A square has 4 equal sides and 4 corners.
- A triangle has 3 sides and 3 corners.
- A rectangle has 4 sides (opposite sides are equal) and 4 corners.

## What you will need

Photocopy master 10 (see page 264)

## Teaching sequence

- Give each pupil one of the four shapes cut from the Photocopy master and ask them to describe each shape.
- Ask pupils to describe the differences between the shapes.
- Ask pupils to work in pairs. One pupil hides a shape and their partner has to guess the shape by asking only two questions. The name of the shape must not be mentioned.

  **Example:**
  *"How many corners does the shape have?"*
  *"Are all the sides equal?"*

---

Unit
**5** Shapes and Patterns

Let's Learn!

**Getting to know shapes**

1 Trace these shapes with your finger. How many sides does each shape have?

0

**circle**

3

**triangle**

4

**square**

4

**rectangle**

54

## Note

Most pupils will know the four shapes but may not know how to describe them in terms of sides and corners. Describe shapes to pupils, using these terms, before asking them to carry out the activity.

## What you will need

- Four shapes (circle, triangle, square, rectangle) cut from Photocopy master 10 (see page 264) for each pair of pupils
- Four shapes in various sizes and colours cut from Photocopy master 11 (see page 265)

## Additional activity

Attach shapes to the board and ask pupils to classify them. Include different sizes, colours and shapes.

---

Shapes and Patterns **Unit 5**

 2

These are circles.

These are triangles.

These are squares.

These are rectangles.

How are squares and rectangles different?

 Which shapes are not squares? How do you know?

This does not have 4 sides that are of the same length.

This does not have straight sides.

This does not have 4 sides.

55

## Teaching sequence

2

- Show pupils a big circle and a smaller circle and ask if they are the same shape.
- Repeat by varying the size and colour of the shapes and ask if the shapes are the same or different. Ask pupils to explain their answers.
- Ask pupils to look at the four groups classified by shape. Ask pupils, "*How is a square different from a rectangle?*". Look for pupils who say that the square has 4 equal sides but the rectangle does not.

3

- Ask pupils to look at the picture and answer the questions.
- Ask pupils to explain why each shape is a square or not a square.
- Look out for pupils who notice that the second shape is a rectangle as it does not have 4 equal sides. Similarly, the fourth shape is a circle as it does not have 4 sides and the last shape is a triangle as it has only 3 sides.

**Independent work**
Practice I in Practice Book IB, pp 5 to 8.

## Teaching sequence

- Ask pupils to work in groups of 4. Give each group the shapes shown in the textbook.
- Ask each group to classify or group the shapes according to the four basic shapes.
- Ask pupils to classify or group the shapes by other characteristics, for example, by colour and size.
- Encourage each group to discuss their answers.

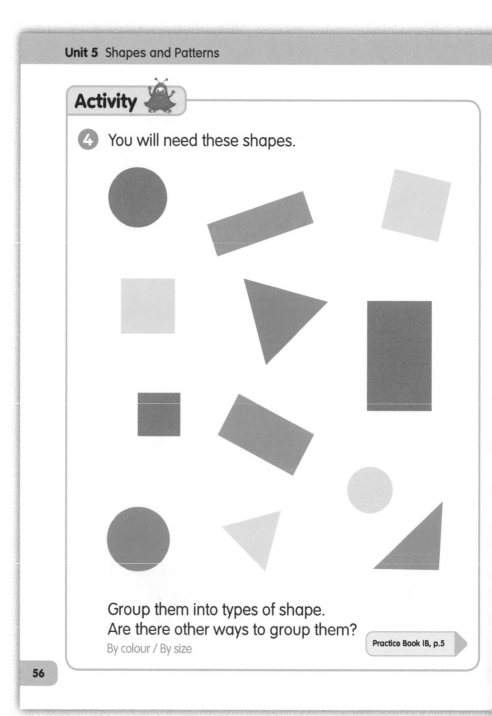

Unit 5  Shapes and Patterns

### Activity

4  You will need these shapes.

Group them into types of shape.
Are there other ways to group them?
By colour / By size

Practice Book IB, p.5

56

## Learning objectives: Making pictures from shapes

**Pupils will be able to:**

- identify the four basic shapes and find the number of each shape in a given picture
- make pictures using the four basic shapes

## Key concept

Shapes such as circles, triangles, squares and rectangles can be used to make pictures.

## What you will need

- Plastic 2D shapes
- Magnets or adhesive tack

### Let's Learn!

**Making pictures from shapes**

1 Here are 2 rectangles, 2 triangles and a square.

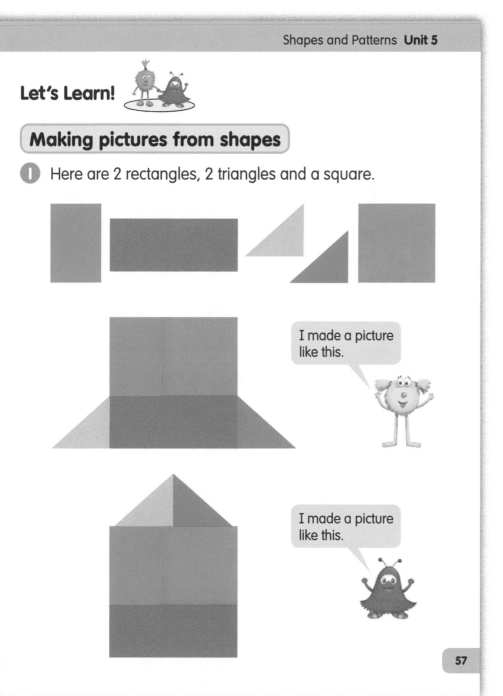

I made a picture like this.

I made a picture like this.

57

## Teaching sequence

1

- Ask pupils to look at the pictures and identify the shapes used to make the two pictures.
- Ask pupils to count the number of shapes used to make the pictures. (2 rectangles, 2 triangles and 1 square)
- Ask pupils to explore other ways in which they could make pictures using the shapes.
- Invite volunteers to make more pictures using the same shapes on the board.

## Additional activity

Ask pupils to work in groups of 4. Give each group a picture, for example, from a magazine. Ask pupils to describe the shapes they see. For example, *"The roof is a triangle."* Explain to pupils that shapes are all around them.

## Teaching sequence

- Ask pupils to look at the picture.
- Ask pupils to work in groups of 4. Ask each group to identify the shapes and count the number of each shape in the picture.
- Invite each group to share their answers and discuss these with the class.

**2** This picture is made up of many shapes.

How many of these shapes can you find?

| Shape | How many? |
|---|---|
| Triangles | 8 |
| Rectangles | 10 |
| Squares | 2 |
| Circles | 10 |

**Home Maths** Encourage your child to identify shapes around the house or in your area, for example, at the park, at the library, or at the supermarket.

58

## What you will need

Coloured sheets of card for each pupil

## Independent work

Practice 2 in Practice Book 1B, pp 9 to 14.

## Activity

**3** Make a picture using paper shapes.

Practice Book 1B, p.9

## Let's Explore!

**4** You will need these shapes.

Make two different pictures using all of these shapes.

Home Maths — Ask your child to use shapes to make lots of different pictures. Encourage your child to use a variety of shapes.

## Teaching sequence

**3**

- Show pupils how to make a picture using shapes cut out of card.
- Ask pupils to make their own pictures using the four basic shapes.

**4** *Let's Explore!*

- Give pupils the shapes (2 similar squares and 2 similar rectangles) and ask them to use these to make two different pictures. (see Photocopy master 12 on page 266).

**Examples:**

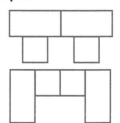

- Invite pupils to share their pictures with the class.

## Learning objectives: Seeing shapes in things around us

**Pupils will be able to:**

- identify the four basic shapes in real-life objects
- name objects that have these basic shapes

## Key concept

When an object is viewed from different angles/sides, we can see different shapes. For example, the top view of a tin of soup is a circle.

## What you will need

- Clock
- Various objects with the four basic shapes, some with more than one shape (e.g. tin of soup, box, etc.)

## Note

The objective here is for pupils to notice that shapes are everywhere and can be easily spotted. Pupils should be encouraged to go beyond just looking for one shape on objects. This links real life to mathematics.

## Teaching sequence

- Ask pupils to look at the picture in the textbook. Show the clock to pupils and ask them what shape the clock is.
- Ask pupils if they have seen other objects that have the shape of a circle.

- Show objects that have the four basic shapes, such as a box and a tin. Ask pupils to identify the shape(s) on each object.
- Ask volunteers to trace one side of the object on the board to show the shape.
- Ask pupils if the objects have more than one shape, and if they say 'yes', ask them to show the class the different shapes on one object. For example, a tin looks like a rectangle from the side but a circle from the top.
- Ask pupils to work in pairs to describe the shapes of the objects in the textbook.

---

**Unit 5  Shapes and Patterns**

**Let's Learn!**

### Seeing shapes in things around us

1  This is a clock.
It has the shape of a circle.

2  Here are some other objects.
What shapes can you see?

rectangle and circles

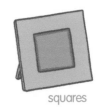
squares

rectangles and squares

triangle

triangle

triangle

square

circles

60

## Thinking skill

Classifying

## What you will need

A cereal box

## Independent work

Practice 3 in Practice Book 1B, pp 15 to 18.

## Additional activities

- Encourage pupils to list objects in their homes that have the four basic shapes.
- Ask pupils to look for or think of more objects that have two different shapes.

---

Shapes and Patterns **Unit 5**

### Activity

③ Look around your classroom and school.

a Name three things that have the shape of a circle.

b Name three things that have the shape of a rectangle.

c Name three things that have the shape of a triangle.

d Name three things that have the shape of a square.

④ Look at this cereal box. What shapes can you see?
circles, rectangles, triangles, squares

⑤ Look at this picture. What shapes can you see?

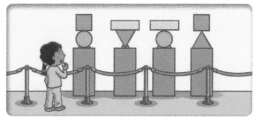

circles, rectangles, triangles and squares

Practice Book 1B, p.15  61

## Teaching sequence

③

- Ask pupils to work in groups. Ask each group to name some things found in the classroom or at school that have the four basic shapes.

  **Examples:**
  square – tabletop, box
  circle – water bottles, pipes
  rectangle – whiteboard, notebooks
  triangle – sandwich, napkin

④

- Show pupils a cereal box.
- Ask pupils to look at the cereal box and point out the shapes found on it.
- Explain to pupils that an object can have more than one shape.

⑤

- Ask pupils to look at and describe the shapes that are on each pedestal. Ask them, "*What shapes can you see?*"

## Learning objectives: Getting to know patterns

**Pupils will be able to:**

- identify and complete a pattern according to one or two attributes: shape, size or colour
- use shapes to make a pattern

## Key concept

Patterns are formed by repeating a particular arrangement of shape, size and/or colour placed next to each other.

## What you will need

Shapes of different colours and sizes

## Notes

- Explain that the word 'pattern' means a special way of arranging the shapes so that they repeat.
- Only one attribute (shape, size or colour) is changed in these activities.

## Teaching sequence

The first pattern

- Ask 8 pupils to hold 4 circles and 4 triangles. Ask them to stand according to the pattern shown: circle, triangle, circle, triangle ...
- Ask pupils to describe what they notice about the way the shapes are placed. Explain to pupils that the shapes follow a pattern.
- Show pupils a red circle, a green circle, a pink square and a blue triangle. Explain to them that the shapes do not follow a pattern.
- Ask pupils to show other ways of rearranging the 8 pupils to form other patterns. For example: circle, circle, triangle, triangle, circle, circle, triangle, triangle.
- Show pupils another pattern that changes only in shape and ask pupils what they notice about the pattern.

The second pattern

- Ask pupils what they notice about the pattern shown.
- Show pupils another pattern that changes only in size and ask pupils what they notice about the pattern.

The third pattern

- Ask pupils what they notice about the pattern shown.
- Show pupils another pattern that changes only in colour and ask pupils what they notice about the pattern.

---

Unit 5 Shapes and Patterns

**Let's Learn!**

**Getting to know patterns**

1 These are patterns.

There is a change in shape.

This pattern repeats.

There is a change in size.

This pattern repeats.

There is a change in colour.

Blue, red, blue, red!

62

## Thinking skill
Identifying patterns

## What you will need
Photocopy master 13
(see page 267)

## Independent work
Practice 4 in Practice Book 1B,
pp 19 to 24.

---

**2** Complete the patterns.

a

(light blue)　(light blue)

b

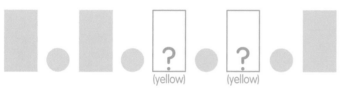
(yellow)　(yellow)

c

(red)　(blue)

d

(yellow)　(pink)

### Activity

**3** Make a pattern using two shapes.
Ask a friend what comes next in the pattern.

Practice Book 1B, p.19

 **Home Maths** There are patterns all around us at home, for example on curtains, wrapping paper, clothes and tiles. Ask your child to look around and see how many patterns they can identify.

63

---

## Teaching sequence

**2**

- Ask pupils to complete the patterns.
- Ask pupils why they chose the particular shape, size or colour for their answers. Ask them to explain which pattern helped them to identify the required shape and its colour or size.

**3**

- Ask pupils to work in pairs to make patterns using two shapes.
- Use only two attributes (shape, colour or size) to make patterns. Ask the first pupil to make a pattern that repeats at least twice.
- Some possible patterns are:
  Change in shape
  Change in size
  Change in colour
  Change in shape and colour
  Change in shape and size
- Ask their partner to guess the shape that comes next and complete the pattern formed.
- Suggest to pupils that a useful technique for them to identify the pattern is to circle the pattern that repeats.

## Learning objectives: Making more patterns

**Pupils will be able to:**

- identify the attributes of size, colour or object in a 3D pattern
- complete a pattern with 3D shapes consisting of cubes, cuboids, cones and cylinders

## Key concept

Patterns can be formed by repeating a particular arrangement of objects placed next to each other.

## What you will need

3D shapes including cubes, cuboids, cylinders and cones of different colours

## Teaching sequence

- Model a pattern with 3D shapes that are the same shape but different in size. Ask pupils what they notice about the pattern.
- Ask pupils how the first pattern was formed.
- Model a pattern with 3D shapes that are the same shape but different in colour. Ask pupils what they notice about the pattern.
- Ask pupils how the second pattern was formed.
- Make a pattern in which there is a change in shape (object). Ask pupils what they notice about the pattern.
- Ask pupils how the third pattern is made.

---

**Unit 5** Shapes and Patterns

## Let's Learn!

### Making more patterns

① These are more patterns.

There is a change in size.

There is a change in colour.

There is a change in object.

64

## Notes

- Help children to identify and name the 3D shapes they are working with.
- Remind pupils that patterns must repeat.

---

Shapes and Patterns **Unit 5**

**2** What comes next?

**a**

  ?

**b**

  ?

**c**

  ?

### Activity

**3** You will need these objects.

Make your own patterns.
Ask a friend to show what comes next.

Practice Book IB, p.25

65

## Teaching sequence

**2**

- Ask pupils to complete the patterns.
- Ask them why they have chosen the particular shape. Encourage them to refer to the pattern to explain their answer. For example, **a** is formed using a small box followed by a larger box (there is a change in size).

**3**

- Ask pupils to work in groups. Give each group the 3D shapes shown. Ask them to make patterns and think of as many ways as possible to make a pattern.
- Invite each group to present their patterns and compare the different patterns made by the different groups.
- Encourage pupils to share and discuss their patterns.

## Objective of activity

**Pupils will be able to:**

- classify shapes by colour and size
- recognise a pattern and identify the missing item

## Thinking skills

- Classifying
- Identifying patterns
- Analysing

## Independent work

*Challenging Practice* and *Problem Solving* in Practice Book IB, pp 27 to 32.

## Teaching sequence

 *Put On Your Thinking Caps!*

**a**

- Ask pupils to look at the shapes in Group A and Group B. Ask pupils, "*How are the groups different?*"

- Encourage as many varied responses as possible. For pupils who need additional support, guide them with questions such as "*What do you notice about the colour of the shapes?*" etc.

- Answers may vary: "*All the shapes in Group A are rectangles and the shapes in Group B are not all rectangles.*"; "*All the shapes in Group A are red and the shapes in Group B are not red.*"; "*Group A contains only I shape and Group B has 4 different shapes.*"

**b**

- Ask pupils to look at the pattern. Ask pupils to explain how they would identify the repeated pattern.

- Ask them to choose the shape that completes the pattern and explain why they chose it.

- The pattern is: medium cylinder, big cube, small cube and big cylinder. Therefore, the answer is the big cylinder, as this is the shape that comes after the small cube.

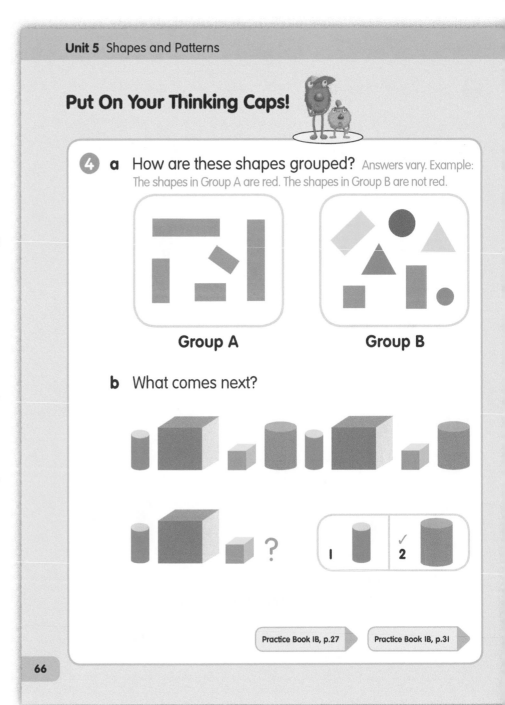

**Unit 5** Shapes and Patterns

## Put On Your Thinking Caps!

**4** **a** How are these shapes grouped? Answers vary. Example: The shapes in Group A are red. The shapes in Group B are not red.

**Group A**     **Group B**

**b** What comes next?

Practice Book IB, p.27     Practice Book IB, p.31

66

INSPIRE MATHS

# PRACTICE BOOK 1B

Consultant and author
Dr Fong Ho Kheong

Authors
Chelvi Ramakrishnan and Bernice Lau Pui Wah

UK consultants
Carole Skinner, Simon d'Angelo and Elizabeth Gibbs


# Unit 5 Shapes and Patterns

Date: ______

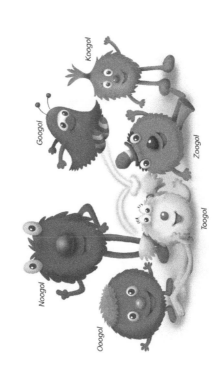

## Practice 1 Getting to know shapes

1 Join the dots. Then name the shapes.

triangle square circle rectangle

**Example**

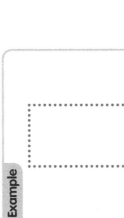

rectangle

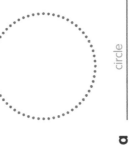

a circle

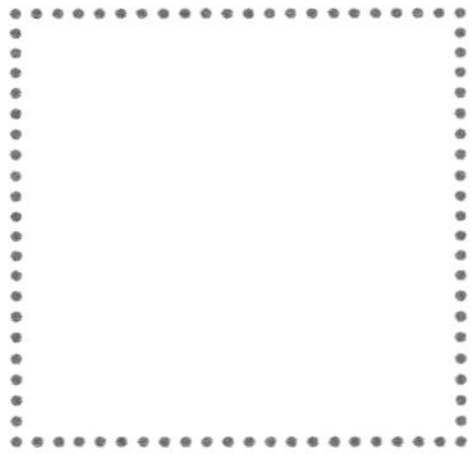

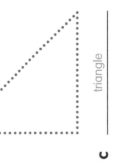

b square

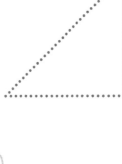

c triangle

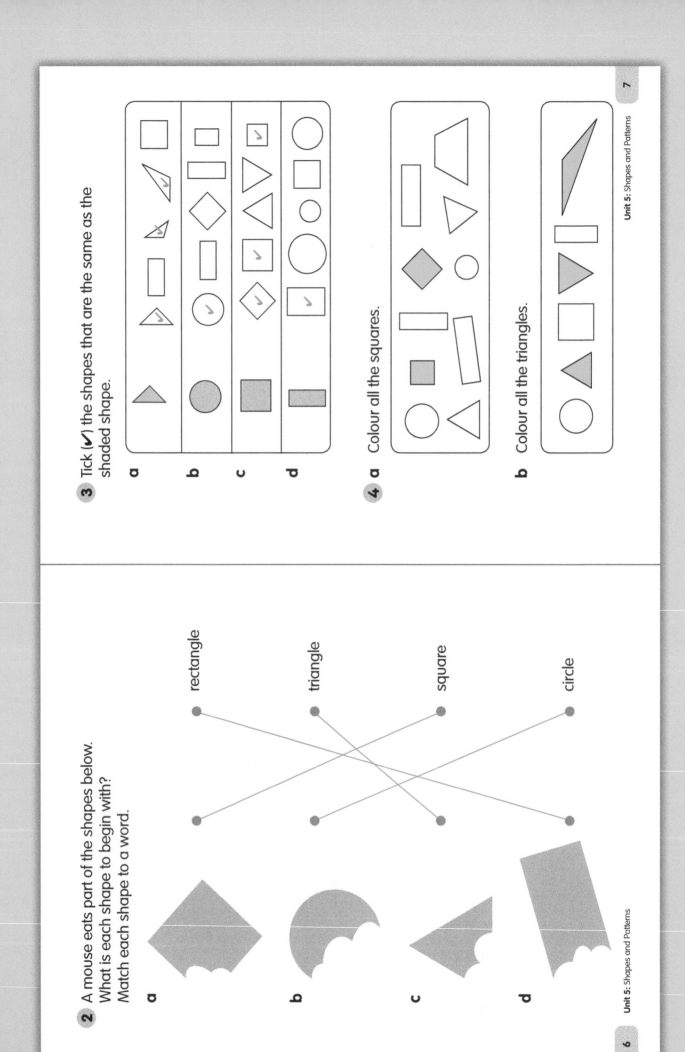

**3** Tick (✔) the shapes that are the same as the shaded shape.

a

b

c

d

**4 a** Colour all the squares.

**b** Colour all the triangles.

**2** A mouse eats part of the shapes below. What is each shape to begin with? Match each shape to a word.

rectangle

triangle

square

circle

a

b

c

d

## Practice 2 — Making pictures from shapes

1 Which shapes make up these pictures?
Tick (✔) the correct boxes.
How many of each shape make up the pictures?

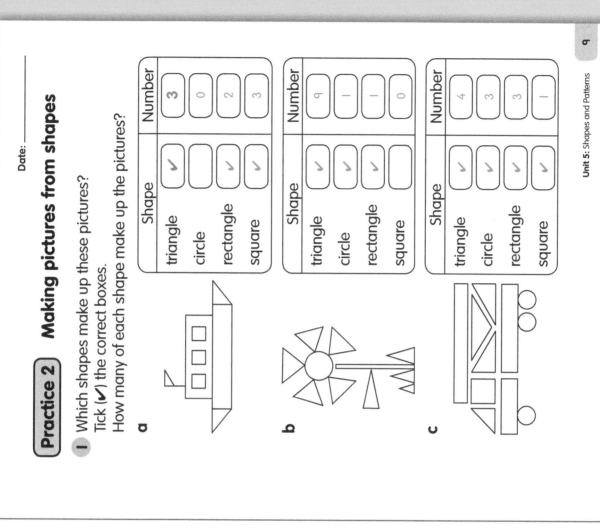

**a**

| Shape | | Number |
|---|---|---|
| triangle | ✔ | 3 |
| circle | | 0 |
| rectangle | ✔ | 2 |
| square | ✔ | 3 |

**b**

| Shape | | Number |
|---|---|---|
| triangle | ✔ | 9 |
| circle | ✔ | 1 |
| rectangle | ✔ | 1 |
| square | | 0 |

**c**

| Shape | | Number |
|---|---|---|
| triangle | ✔ | 4 |
| circle | ✔ | 3 |
| rectangle | ✔ | 3 |
| square | ✔ | 1 |

---

**c** Colour all the rectangles.

**d** Colour all the shapes that are **not** circles.

5 Which shape is **not** in each set?

circle    rectangle    square    triangle

**Set A**

The _square_ is not in Set A.

**Set B**

The _circle_ is not in Set B.

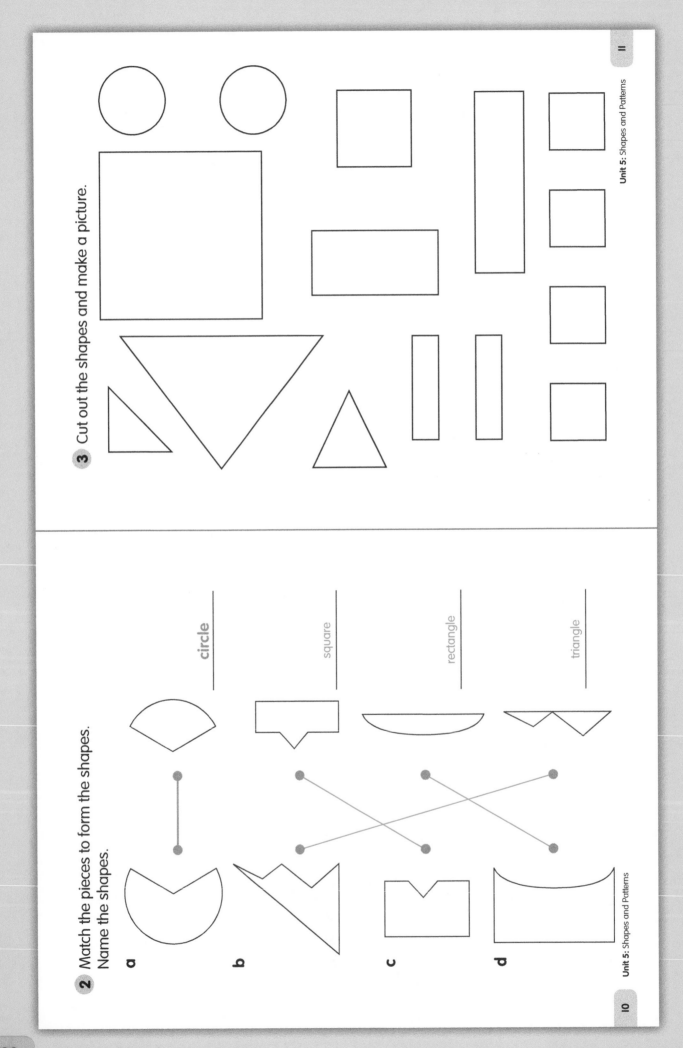

**3** Cut out the shapes and make a picture.

**2** Match the pieces to form the shapes.
Name the shapes.

a

b

c

d

circle

square

rectangle

triangle

4 Draw a picture using triangles, circles, squares and rectangles.

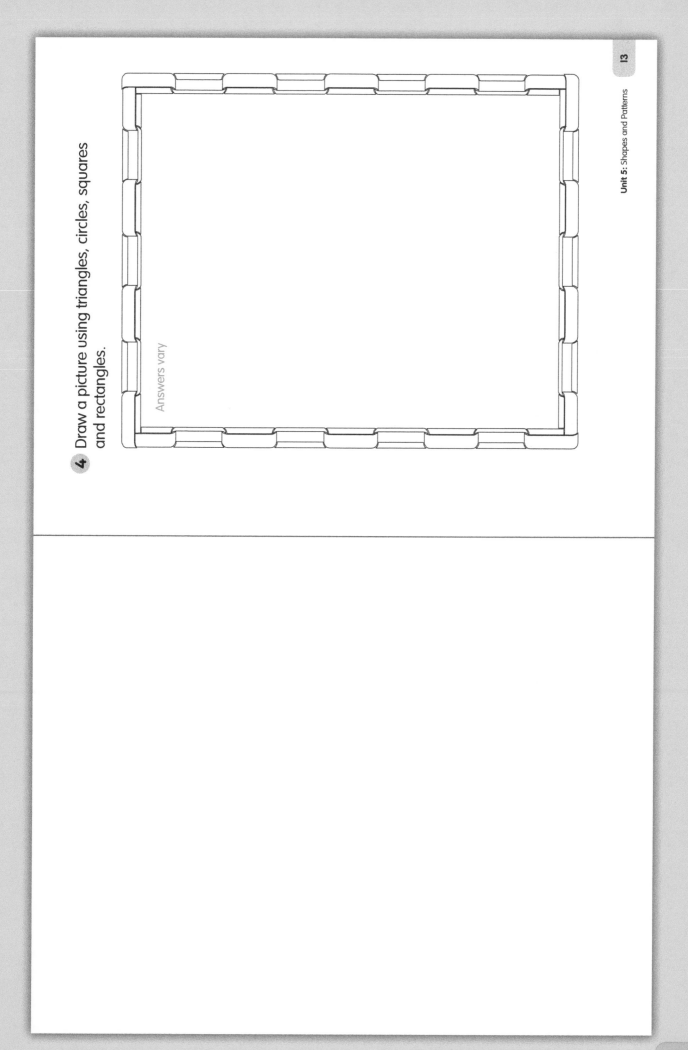

Answers vary

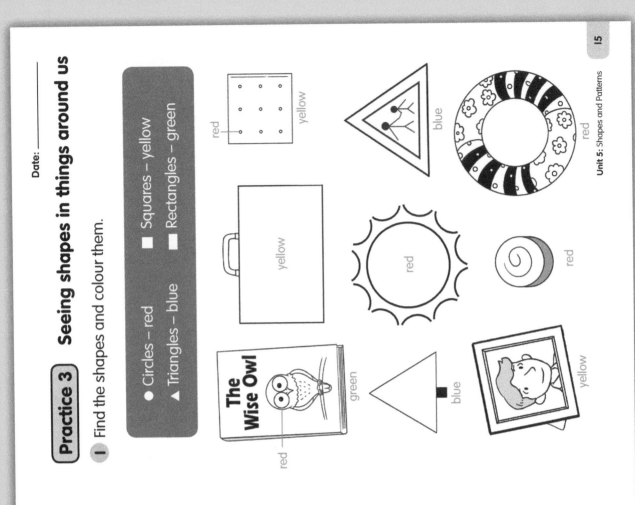

Date: _____

## Practice 3  Seeing shapes in things around us

1  Find the shapes and colour them.

● Circles – red       ■ Squares – yellow
▲ Triangles – blue    ■ Rectangles – green

red

yellow

yellow

red

The Wise Owl
red

green

blue

blue

blue

red

yellow

red

---

5  a  Look at the picture.
How many rectangles can you see?

___2___

b  A star can be made of triangles.

**Example**

This star is made of ___10___ triangles.

Draw triangles in another way to make this star.

This star is made
of  Answers vary  triangles.

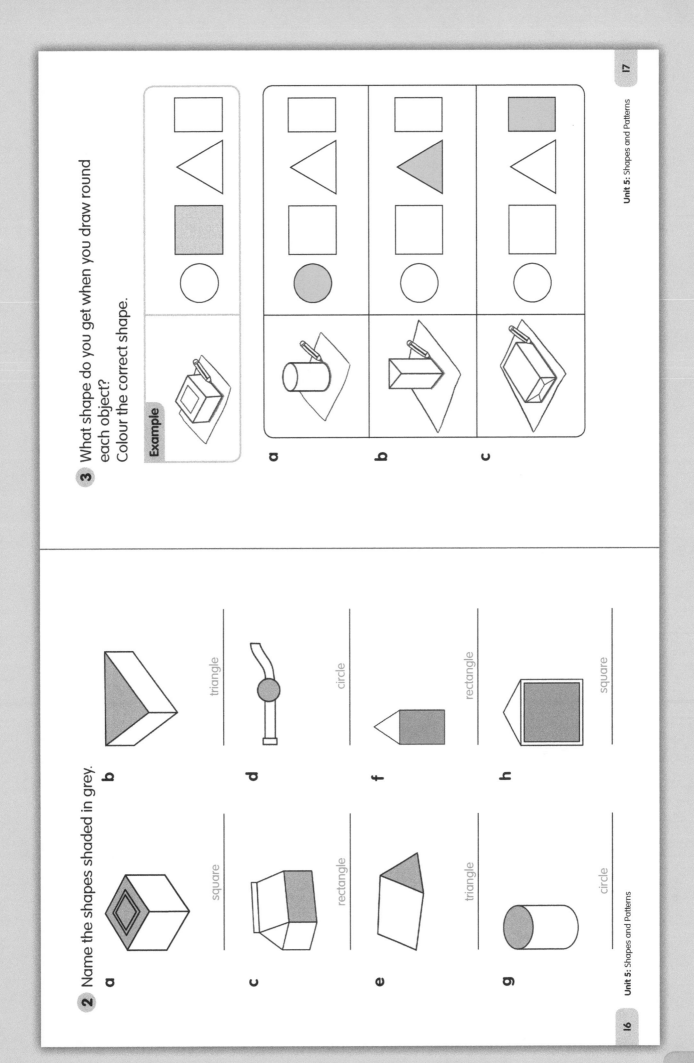

**2** Name the shapes shaded in grey.

a
___ square

b
___ triangle

c
___ rectangle

d
___ circle

e
___ triangle

f
___ rectangle

g
___ circle

h
___ square

**3** What shape do you get when you draw round each object?
Colour the correct shape.

**Example**

a

b

c

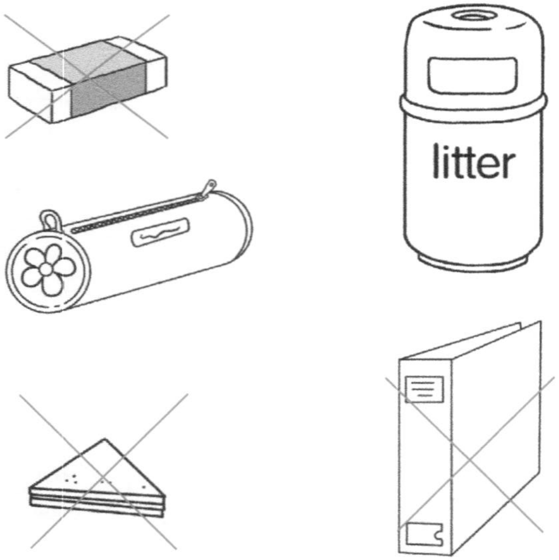

Date: _____

## Practice 4   Getting to know patterns

**1** The shapes below have numbers on them.

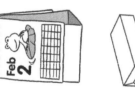

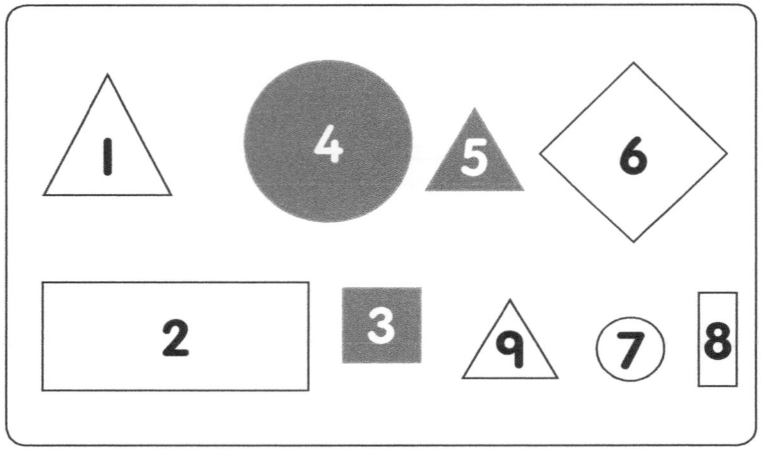

Write the numbers in the correct boxes.

| Circles | Triangles | Rectangles | Squares |
|---|---|---|---|
| 4, 7 | 1, 5, 9 | 2, 8 | 3, 6 |

**4 a**   Circle the objects that have the shape of a square.

**b**   Cross out (**✗**) the objects that do **not** have the shape of a circle.

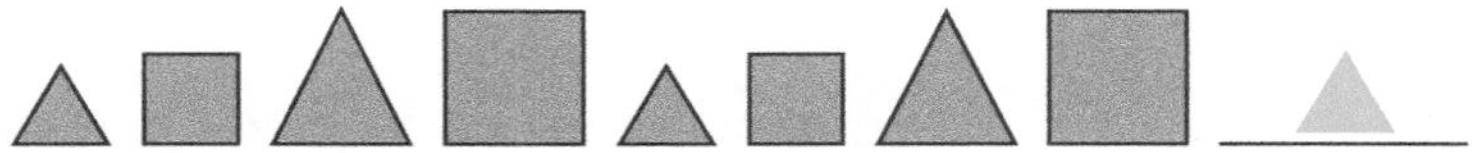

**3** Look at each pattern.
Tick (✔) the shape that comes next.

Example

a

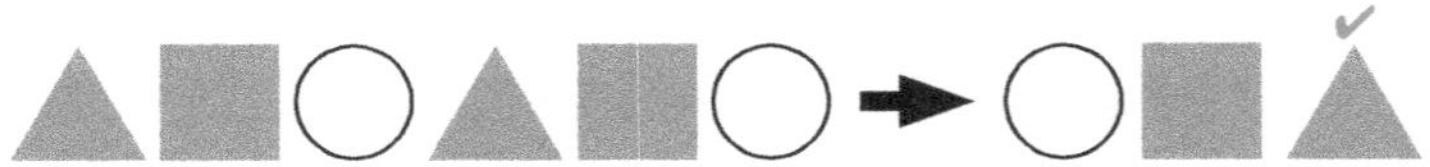

b

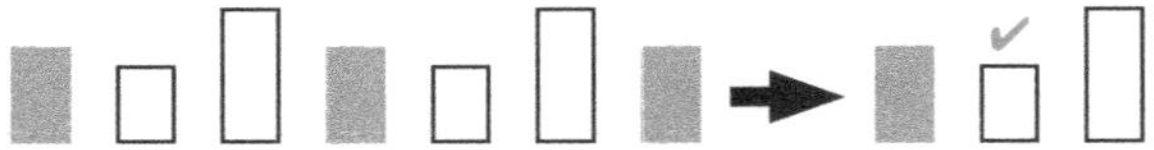

c

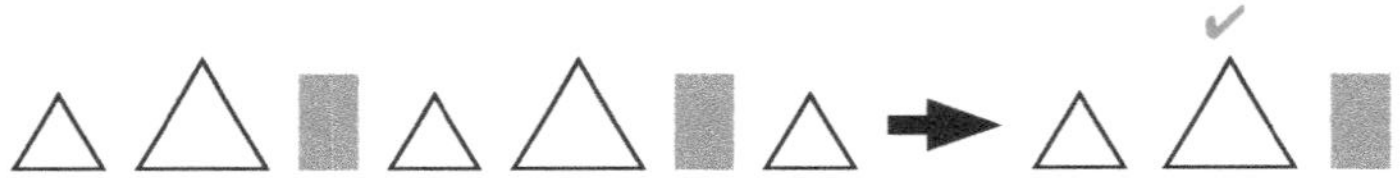

d

**2** Complete the patterns.

Example

a

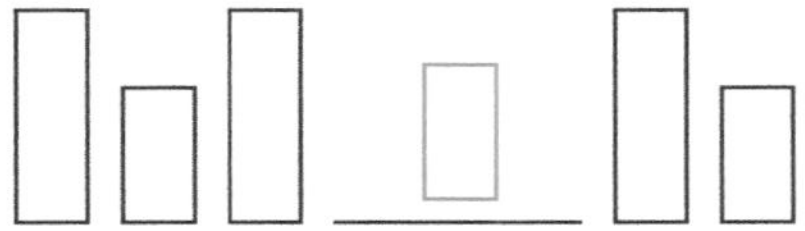

b

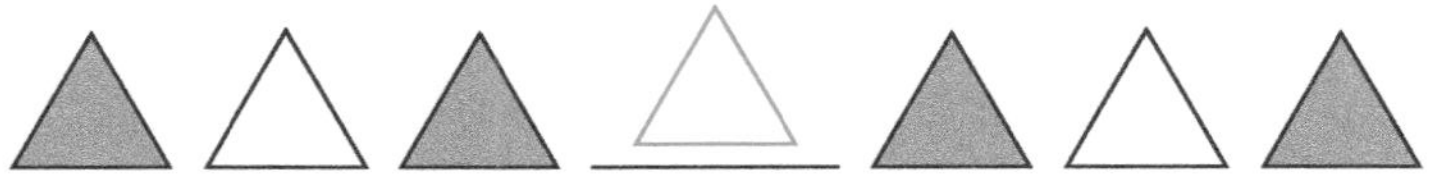

c

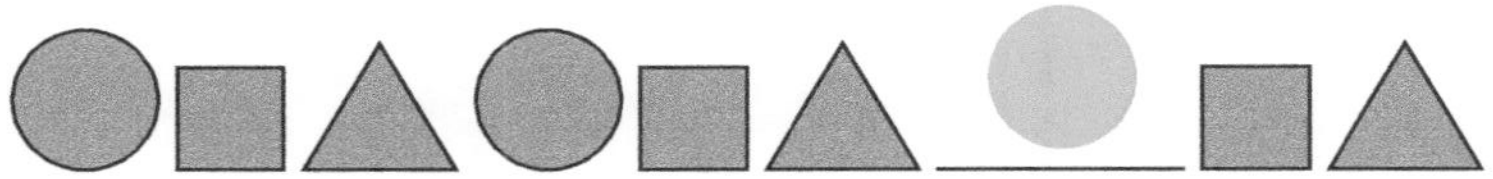

d

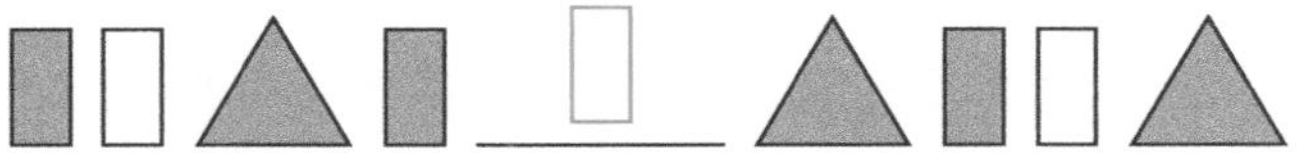

e

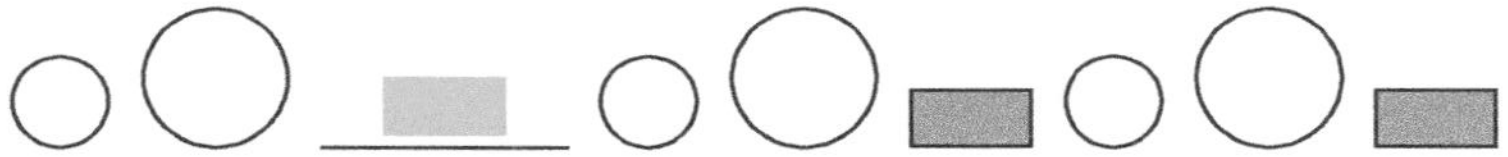

f

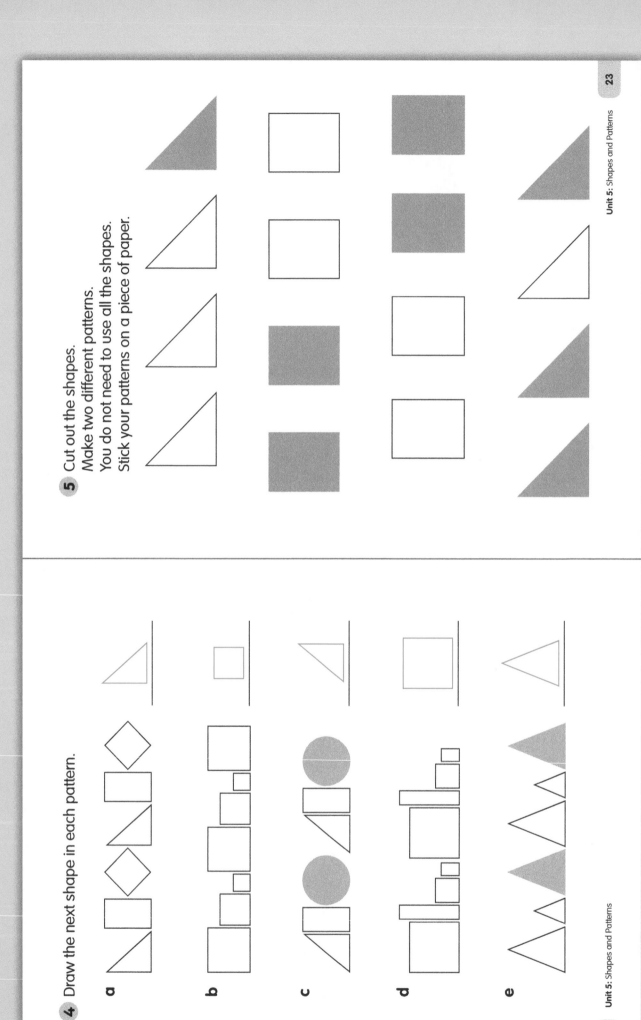

**5** Cut out the shapes.
Make two different patterns.
You do not need to use all the shapes.
Stick your patterns on a piece of paper.

**4** Draw the next shape in each pattern.

a

b

c

d

e

Date: ____________

## Practice 5 Making more patterns

1 What is missing in each pattern?
Tick (✔) the correct answer.

**a**

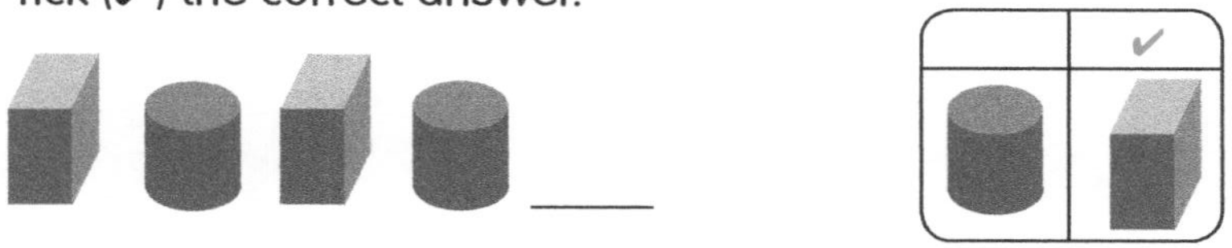


**b**

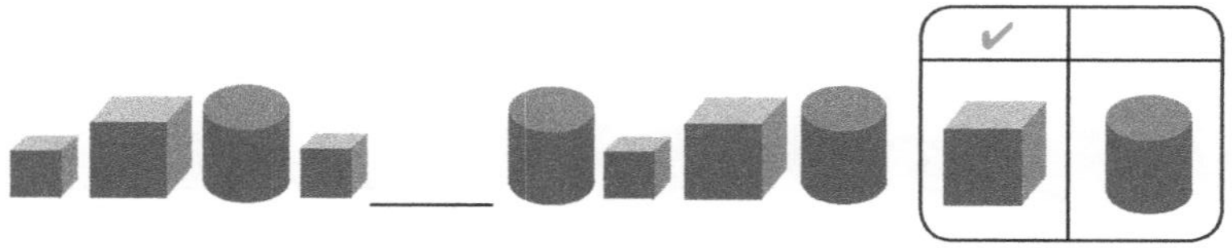


**c**

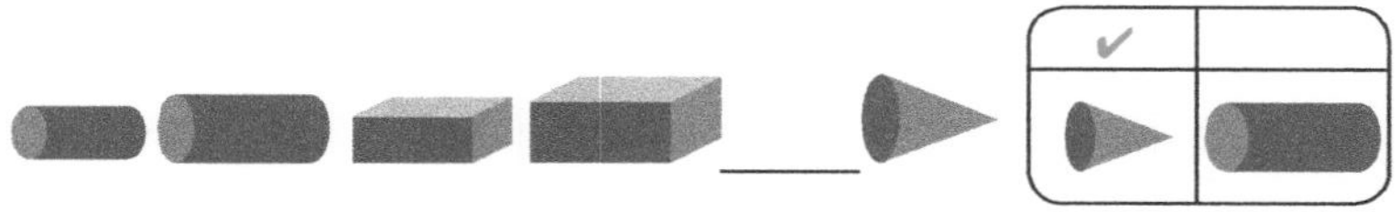


**d**

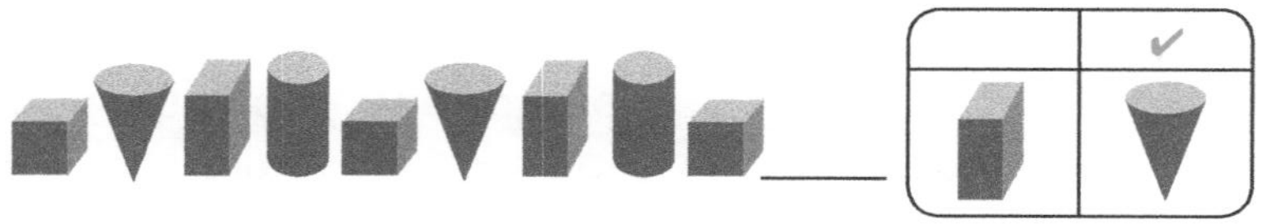


**e**

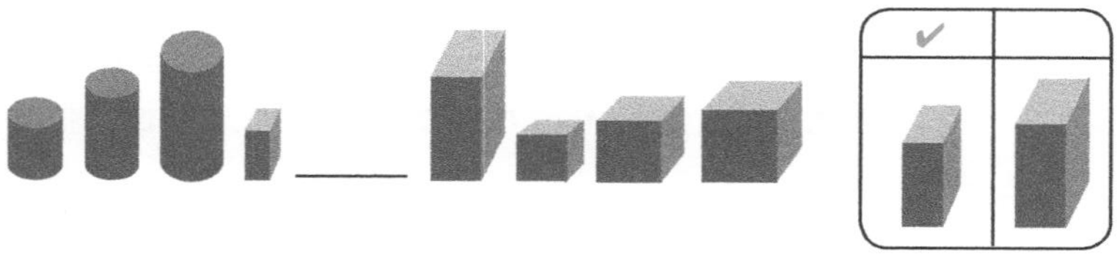

## Challenging Practice

**1** Jack, Farha, Omar and Ella have some shapes.
Which shapes do they have?

**Clues**

- Jack has fewer circles than Farha.
- All of Omar's shapes have 3 sides or more.
- Farha has 4 types of shapes.
- Ella has no squares.

Write the name of the child by the correct set of shapes.

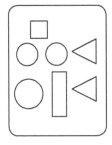

Farha

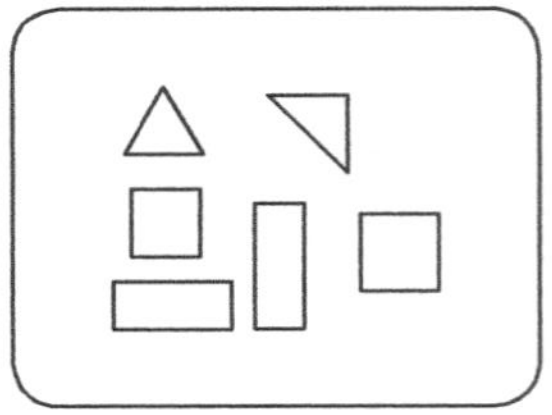

Ella

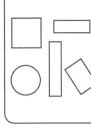

Jack

Omar

---

**2** Circle the mistake in the pattern.
Tick (✔) the correct shape.

Example

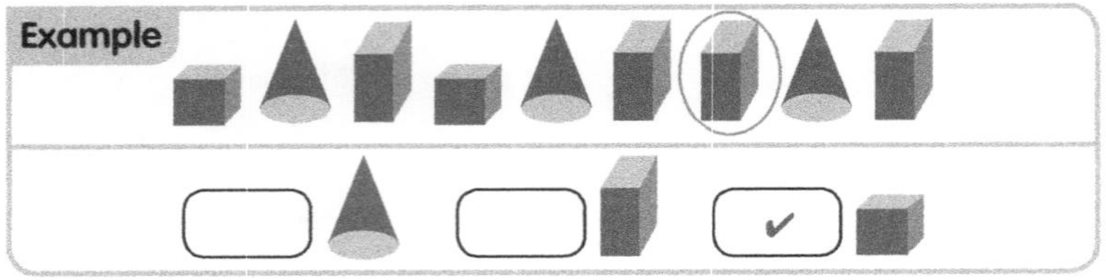

a

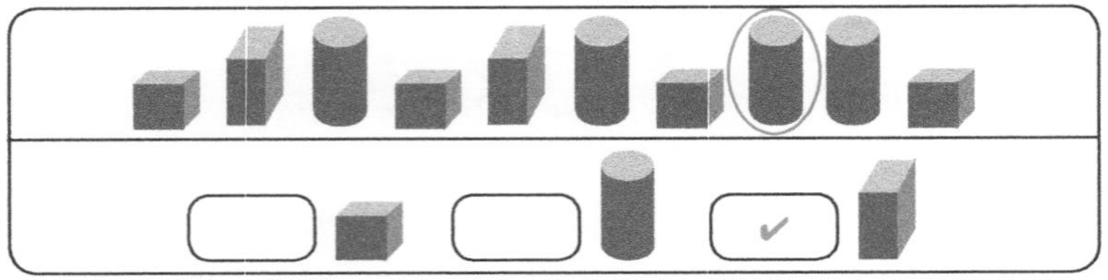

b

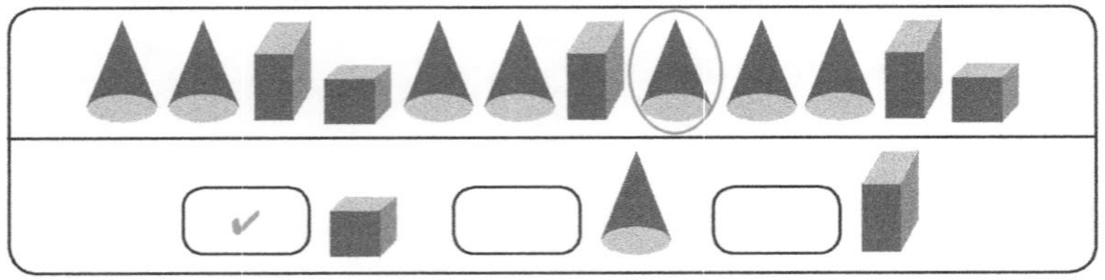

c

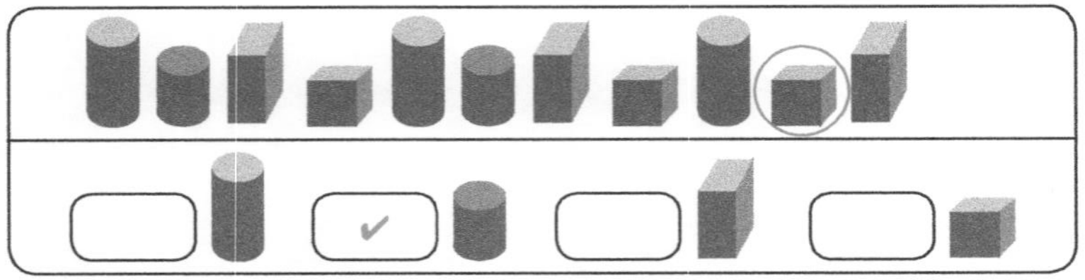

d

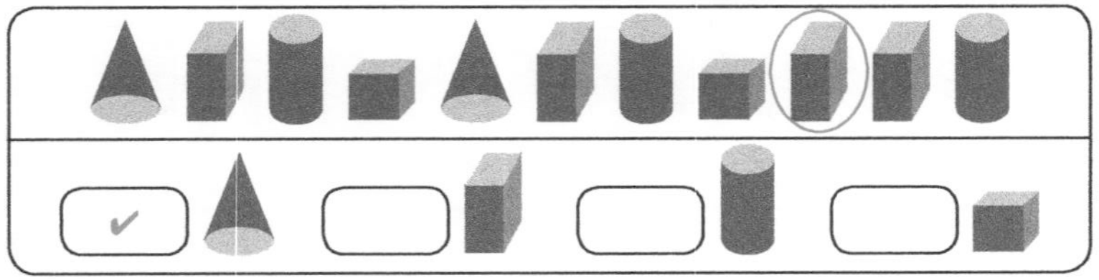

Cut out each shape along the lines.

a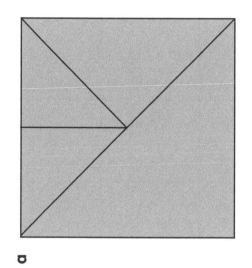

b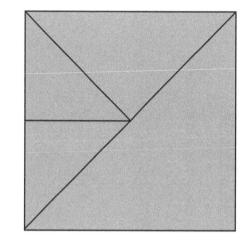

2 Cut out the shapes on page 29.
Arrange the pieces to make the pictures below.
Stick your pictures on a piece of paper.

a

b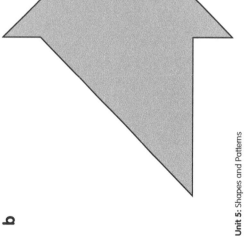

Date: _____

## Problem Solving

1 Draw a shape in each box.
Each row ( ↔ ) and column ( ↕ ) must have these four
shapes: ○ △ ▢ ▭.    Answers vary

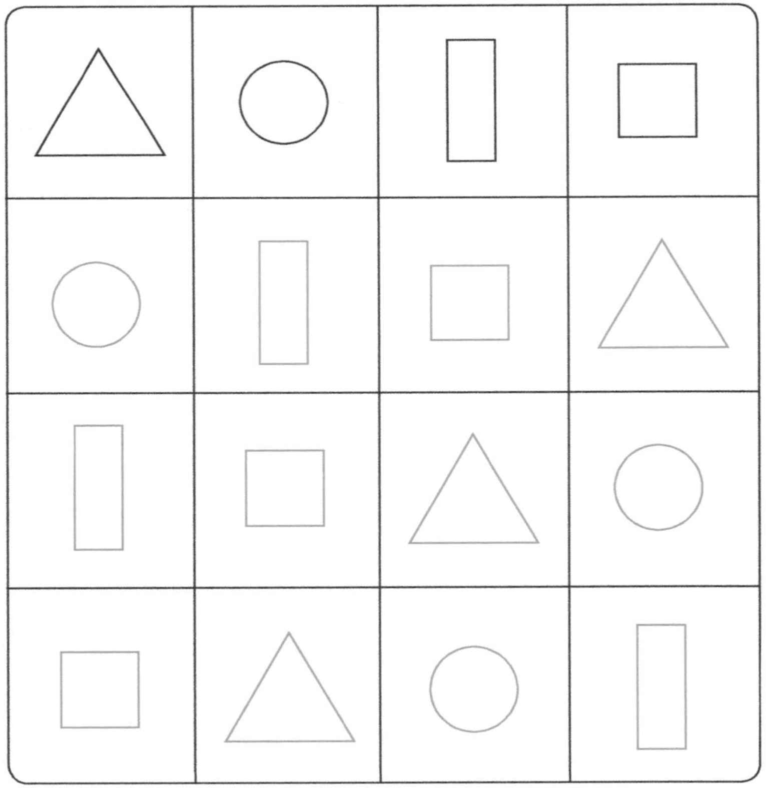

| ▢ | ▭ | ○ | △ |
|---|---|---|---|
| △ | ▢ | ▭ | ○ |
| ○ | △ | ▢ | ▭ |
| ▭ | ○ | △ | ▢ |

**2** Use these shapes to make two patterns.

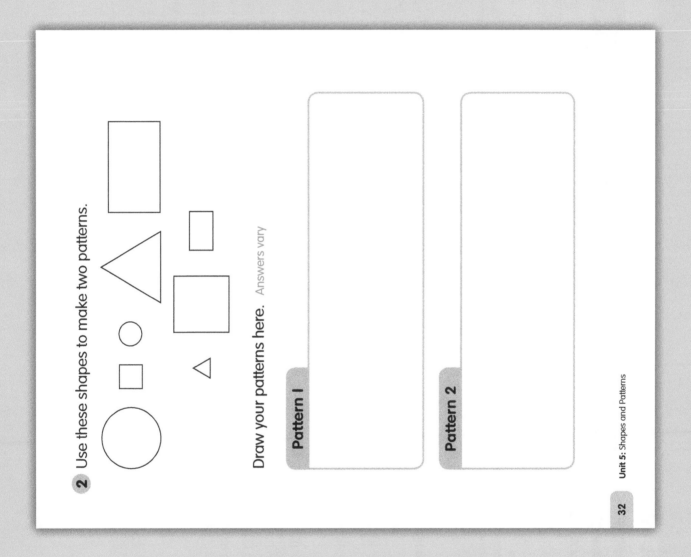

Draw your patterns here. *Answers vary*

**Pattern 1**

**Pattern 2**

Unit 5: Shapes and Patterns

**Answers Unit 5:** Shapes and Patterns 133

| Week | Learning Objectives | Thinking Skills | Resources |
|---|---|---|---|
| 1 | **(1) Knowing ordinal numbers**<br><br>Pupils will be able to:<br>• describe positions using ordinal numbers and words: 1st to 10th and first to tenth<br>• use the words 'before', 'between' and 'after' to describe the position of something<br>• use the words 'first' and 'last' to describe the position of something | • Sequencing | • Pupil Textbook IA, pp 67 to 72<br>• Practice Book IB, pp 33 to 38<br>• Teacher's Guide IA, pp 135 to 140 |
| 1 | **(2) Naming left and right positions**<br><br>Pupils will be able to:<br>• describe positions from the left and right using ordinal numbers<br>• use 'next to' to describe the position of an object<br><br>*Let's Explore!*<br><br>Pupils will be able to investigate and hypothesise a pattern describing the sum of number positions. | • Sequencing<br>• Identifying relationships | • Pupil Textbook IA, pp 73 to 76<br>• Practice Book IB, pp 39 to 42<br>• Teacher's Guide IA, pp 141 to 144 |
| 1 | *Put On Your Thinking Caps!*<br><br>Pupils will be able to make deductions based on the position of object(s) from given suggestions in order to solve the problem. | • Sequencing<br>• Identifying relationships | • Pupil Textbook IA, pp 77 to 78<br>• Practice Book IB, pp 43 to 46<br>• Teacher's Guide IA, p 145 |
| | Review 3 | | • Practice Book IB, pp 47 to 50 |

# Ordinal Numbers

**Learning objectives: Knowing ordinal numbers**

**Pupils will be able to:**

- describe positions using ordinal numbers and words: 1st to 10th and first to tenth
- use the words 'before', 'between' and 'after' to describe the position of something

- use the words 'first' and 'last' to describe the position of something

**Key concept**

Ordinal numbers are for describing the position of something.

---

**Unit 6** Ordinal Numbers

Let's Learn!

**Knowing ordinal numbers**

1 There are 5 thirsty children.

Farha
Ruby
Ella
Peter
Jack

| 1st first | 2nd second | 3rd third | 4th fourth | 5th fifth |

Ella is **before** Farha .

Peter is **after** Farha .

Farha is **between** Ella **and** Peter .

Describe the positions of Ruby and Jack using these words:

before    after    between

Ruby is before Jack.
Ruby is between Peter and Jack.
Ruby is after Peter.
Jack is after Ruby.

67

**Teaching sequence**

1

- Invite five volunteers to make a line in front of the board.
- Use ordinal numbers 1st to 5th to describe their positions. Write the ordinal numbers on the board above each volunteer.
- Point out the difference between ordinal numbers (1st, 2nd ...) and counting numbers (1, 2 ...). Explain that the last pupil in the line is the fifth pupil, because there are 5 pupils in the line.
- Introduce the word forms of ordinal numbers first to fifth.
- Use terms such as 'before', 'after' and 'between' when describing positions.
- Work through the examples in the textbook together.
- Invite five more volunteers to the line to teach 6th to 10th.
- Emphasise to pupils that the last pupil in the line is now the tenth pupil, because there are now 10 pupils in the line.
- Introduce the word forms of ordinal numbers sixth to tenth.
- Reinforce the terms 'before', 'after' and 'between' when describing positions.

# Thinking skill
Sequencing

## Teaching sequence

- Ask pupils to look carefully at the picture. Ask pupils to tell stories using the following words:
  - (1) first
  - (2) last
  - (3) Omar, before
  - (4) Omar, after
  - (5) Tai, before
  - (6) Tai, between

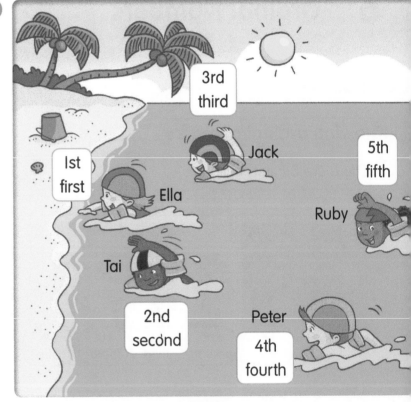

**Unit 6** Ordinal Numbers

3rd
third

Jack

5th
fifth

1st
first

Ella

Ruby

Tai

2nd
second

Peter

4th
fourth

**a**  Which children are before Ruby? ⬚  Ella, Tai, Jack and Peter

**b**  Who will be first to the beach? ⬚ Ella

68

## Additional activity

Ask pupils to work in pairs.

Each pair should write five sentences using the following words:

- ordinal numbers (1st to 10th)
- before
- after
- between
- next to

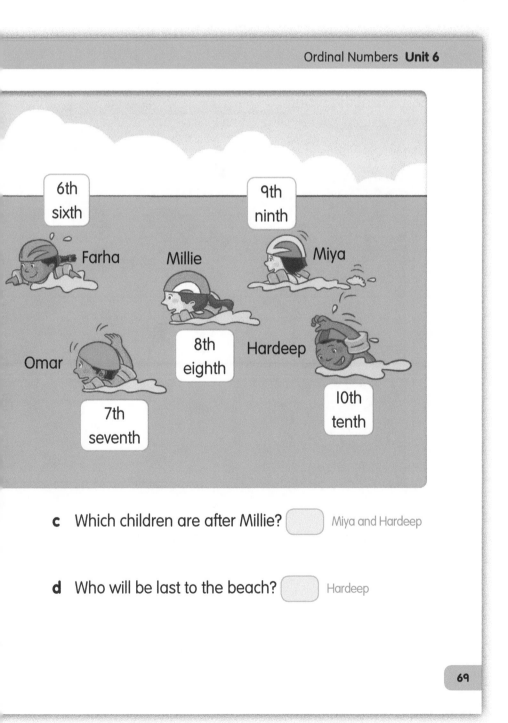

**c** Which children are after Millie? [ ] Miya and Hardeep

**d** Who will be last to the beach? [ ] Hardeep

69

## Additional activity
Reinforce the concept using fridge or board magnets to represent the position of children in other races.

## Teaching sequence

- Work through the examples in the textbook together.
- Point out that this is a race, and the person at the top of the climbing wall is considered to be first.
- Ask pupils to discuss the questions and share their answers.

**3** Look at the picture.

**a** How many children are climbing the wall? [ 6 ]

**b** Who is 1st? [ Ruby ]

**c** Who is last? [ Jack ]

**d** Who is 2nd? [ Peter ]

70

**e** Who is 4th? [ Ella ]

**f** Where is Millie? [     ] 5th / Fifth

**g** Who is just after Millie? [ Jack ]

**h** Who is just before Ella? [ Tai ]

71

## Independent work

Practice I in Practice Book IB, pp 33 to 38.

## Additional activity

Ask pupils to work in pairs. Ask each pair to draw a picture of a building with 3 or more floors. Ask them to draw some of their classmates on each floor. Invite pupils to describe the picture.

## Teaching sequence

- Ask pupils to look carefully at the picture in the textbook.
- Ask them to name the floors and describe what is happening on each floor.
- Ask pupils to discuss the questions and share their answers.

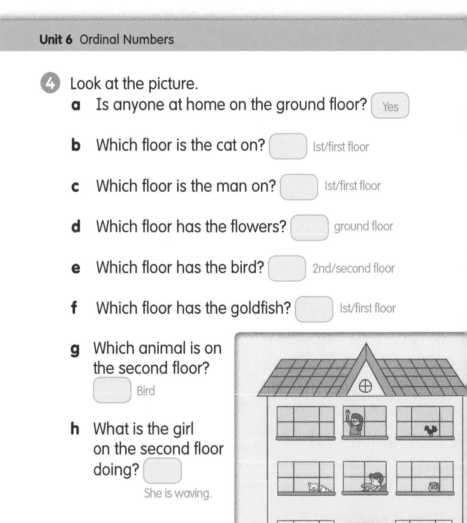

**Unit 6** Ordinal Numbers

④ Look at the picture.

**a** Is anyone at home on the ground floor? [ Yes ]

**b** Which floor is the cat on? [ ] lst/first floor

**c** Which floor is the man on? [ ] lst/first floor

**d** Which floor has the flowers? [ ] ground floor

**e** Which floor has the bird? [ ] 2nd/second floor

**f** Which floor has the goldfish? [ ] lst/first floor

**g** Which animal is on the second floor? [ ] Bird

**h** What is the girl on the second floor doing? [ ] She is waving.

72

Home Maths — Remind your child that the first floor is the floor above the ground floor.

Practice Book IB, p.33

**Pupils will be able to:**

- describe positions from the left and right using ordinal numbers
- use 'next to' to describe the position of an object

## Key concept

Positions from the left and right can be named using ordinal numbers.

---

# Let's Learn!

## Naming left and right positions

The T-shirt is first from the **left**.
The dress is second from the left.

The T-shirt is fifth from the **right**.
It is also last from the right.

The towel is third from the left.
It is also third from the right.

The jeans are between the towel and the skirt.

73

## Teaching sequence

**1**

- Invite five volunteers to make a line in front of the board. Use ordinal numbers to describe their positions. Write the ordinal numbers on the board. Use terms such as 'between' and 'next to' to describe the clothes.

  **Examples:**
  *"Rosa is first from the left."*
  *"Ben is first from the right."*
  *"Peter is between Rosa and Ben."*

- Work through the examples in the textbook together.

## Thinking skills

- Sequencing
- Identifying relationships

## Teaching sequence

- Invite five more volunteers to the line and ask further questions.

  **Examples:**

  *"Who is second from the right?"*

  *"Where is Abby?"*

- Work through the examples in the textbook together.
- Look for pupils who use ordinal numbers and the terms correctly.

**Unit 6** Ordinal Numbers

Peter    Farha    Ella    Miya    Oma

Left

Peter is **next to** Farha.
Ella is also next to Farha.

Peter is 1st from the left.
He is also 10th or last from the right.

Farha is 2nd from the left.
She is also 9th from the right.

74

**142**    **Unit 6:** Ordinal Numbers

**Independent work**

Practice 2 in Practice Book IB,
pp 39 to 42.

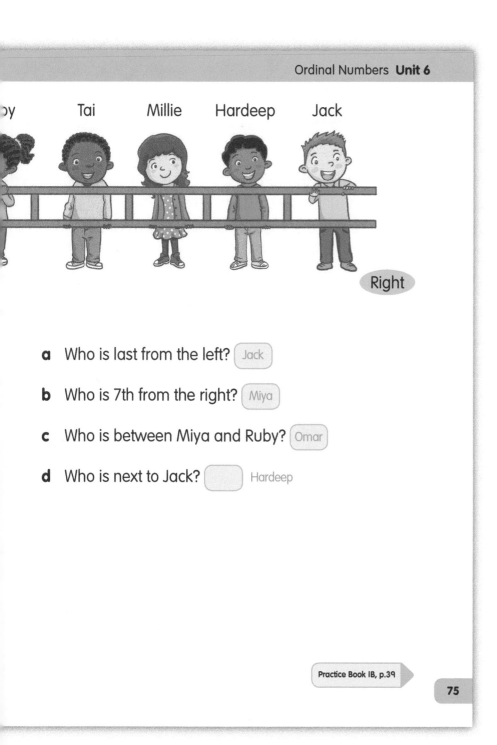

by    Tai    Millie    Hardeep    Jack

Right

**a** Who is last from the left? [ Jack ]

**b** Who is 7th from the right? [ Miya ]

**c** Who is between Miya and Ruby? [ Omar ]

**d** Who is next to Jack? [    ] Hardeep

Practice Book IB, p.39

75

## Objective of activity

**Pupils will be able to:**

- investigate and hypothesise a pattern describing the sum of number positions.

## What you will need

- A set of 9 blue cards and I red card for each group
- Photocopy master 14 (see page 268)

## Teaching sequence

**3** *Let's Explore!*

- Ask pupils to work in groups to discuss the questions and carry out the activity.
- Encourage pupils to look for patterns.
- Ask pupils to discuss the questions and share their answers.

---

### Let's Explore!

**3** You will need a set of 9 blue cards and I red card.

**1** Shuffle the cards.
Arrange the cards in a row.

**2** Count and record the following in a chart.
What is the position of the red card from the left?
What is the position of the red card from the right?

| No. | Position of red card from the left | Position of red card from the right | ⬚ + ⬚ |
|---|---|---|---|
| I | ⬚ | ⬚ | ⬚ |
| 2 | ⬚ | ⬚ | ⬚ |
| 3 | ⬚ | ⬚ | ⬚ |
| 4 | ⬚ | ⬚ | ⬚ |

**3** Shuffle the cards.
Repeat the activity.
Write your answers in a chart.

The total number of cards is 10.

The answer in the ⬚ is always I more than the total number of cards.

76

---

## Thinking skills
- Sequencing
- Identifying relationships

## Objective of activity
**Pupils will be able to:**
- make deductions based on the position of the object(s) from given suggestions to solve the problem.

## Teaching sequence

**④** *Put On Your Thinking Caps!*

- Encourage pupils to read the instructions and place the person or object in the correct box.
- Encourage pupils to use diagrams to show alternative solutions.

---

Ordinal Numbers **Unit 6**

# Put On Your Thinking Caps!

**④** Put the people and objects in the correct order.

**a** Ruby, Jack and Miya are in a row.
Ruby is last.
Jack is not 2nd.

 Jack    Miya   Ruby

Ist          3rd

Who is in the middle?   Miya
How do you know?   Since Ruby is last, only Jack and Miya can be 2nd. Since Jack is not 2nd, Miya must be 2nd.

**b** Hardeep plants 4 flowers in a row.
The lily is not 2nd from the left.
The daisy is between the rose and the sunflower.
The sunflower is Ist from the right.

 lily    rose    daisy    sunflower

Left                 Right

Which flower is 3rd from the right?   rose
How do you know?
Since the sunflower is Ist from the right, it cannot be the 3rd from the right.
Since the lily is not 2nd from the left, it cannot be 3rd from the right.
The daisy must be 2nd from the right since it is between the rose and sunflower.
Therefore the rose is 3rd from the right.

77

## Independent work

*Challenging Practice, Problem Solving, Maths Journal* and Review 3 in Practice Book IB, pp 43 to 50.

## Teaching sequence

**5** *Put On Your Thinking Caps!*

Ask pupils to apply the investigation results from *Let's Explore!* to solve these problems.

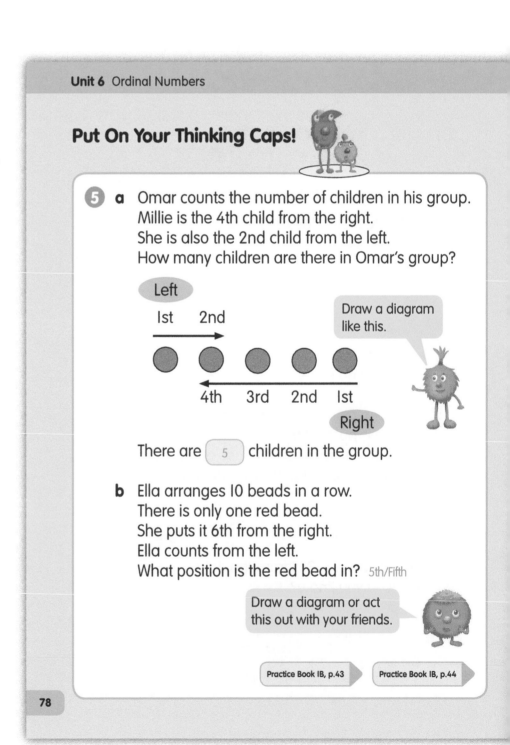

Unit 6  Ordinal Numbers

# Put On Your Thinking Caps!

**5 a** Omar counts the number of children in his group.
Millie is the 4th child from the right.
She is also the 2nd child from the left.
How many children are there in Omar's group?

Left
Ist    2nd

Draw a diagram like this.

4th    3rd    2nd    Ist
Right

There are ⬚ 5 ⬚ children in the group.

**b** Ella arranges 10 beads in a row.
There is only one red bead.
She puts it 6th from the right.
Ella counts from the left.
What position is the red bead in? 5th/Fifth

Draw a diagram or act this out with your friends.

Practice Book IB, p.43        Practice Book IB, p.44

78

# Unit 6 — Ordinal Numbers

**Practice 1**  Knowing ordinal numbers

1 Circle:

**a**  the 1st flower

**b**  the 5th dog

**c**  the 8th car

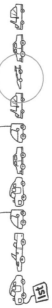

**d**  the 6th duckling

**2** Colour:

**a** 3 birds   *Answers vary*

the 3rd bird

**b** 7 beads   *Answers vary*

the 7th bead

**c** 9 ants   *Answers vary*

the 9th ant

(3rd)

**d** 1 frog   *Answers vary*

the 1st frog

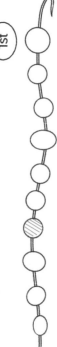

(5th)

**4** Look at the picture.

Ruby Hardeep Millie Tai Miya Peter Ella Omar Farha Jack

Fill in the spaces.

**a** Miya is ___fifth / 5th___ in the queue.

**b** The ___ninth / 9th___ child in the queue is Farha.

**c** Farha is just after ___Omar___.

**d** Millie is just before ___Tai___.

**e** Miya does not want to wait. She walks away. Now Omar is ___seventh / 7th___ in the queue.

**f** Someone wants to join the queue. He should stand after ___Jack___.

---

**3** Match.

first — 1st
second — 3rd
third — 2nd
fourth — 5th
fifth — 4th
sixth — 7th
seventh — 10th
eighth — 6th
ninth — 8th
tenth — 9th

## Page 38

**5** Look at the picture.

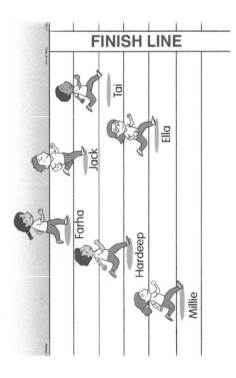

FINISH LINE

Farha　Jack　Tai
Hardeep　Ella
Millie

Fill in the spaces.

**a** Who is second in the race? _____ Ella

**b** Who is fifth in the race? _____ Hardeep

**c** Where is Tai? _____ First / 1st

**d** Who is between Farha and Millie? _____ Hardeep

**e** Who is just before Hardeep? _____ Farha

**f** Who is after Hardeep? _____ Millie

## Page 39

Date: _____

### Practice 2　Naming left and right positions

**1** Colour:

**a** the 4th bird from the left

Left 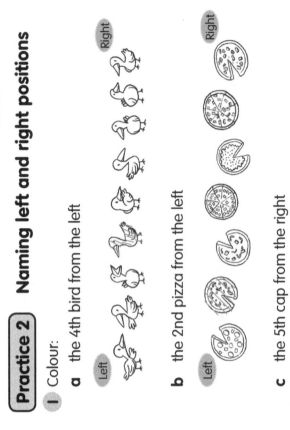 Right

**b** the 2nd pizza from the left

Left Right

**c** the 5th cap from the right

Left  Right

**2** Draw:

**a** an apple on the last plate from the right

**b** a fish on the 6th plate from the left

Left  Right

**3** Answer the question using the clues.

**Where do kangaroos live?**

| A | U | S | T | R | A | L | I | A |
|---|---|---|---|---|---|---|---|---|
| 1 | 2 | 3 | 4 | 5 | 6 | 7 | 8 | 9 |

Clues:

Left    T  R  S  A  L  U  I    Right

1  4th letter from the left.
2  2nd letter from the right.
3  3rd letter from the left.
4  1st letter from the left.
5  6th letter from the right.
6  4th letter from the right.
7  letter next to U on the left.
8  1st letter from the right.
9  letter between S and L.

**4** Look at the picture.

Blue  Brown  Purple  Black  Orange  Yellow  Green  Pink  Red

Colour in the order given.

- The third coach from the right is **green**.
- The fifth coach from the left is **orange**.
- The seventh coach from the right is **purple**.
- The last coach from the right is **blue**.
- The coach between the purple and orange coaches is **black**.
- The coach next to the blue coach is **brown**.
- The eighth coach from the left is **pink**.
- The coach just before the pink coach is **red**.
- The coach just after the green coach is **yellow**.

## Challenging Practice

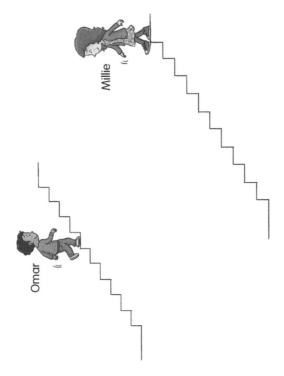

1. When Omar climbs up four steps, he will be on the tenth step.
   Omar is on the __6th / sixth__ step now.

2. When Millie walks down three steps, she will be on the seventh step.
   Millie is on the __10th / tenth__ step now.

---

5. Peter is standing in a row with other children.
   He is 2nd from the right and 8th from the left.
   Draw Peter and the other children.
   Circle Peter.

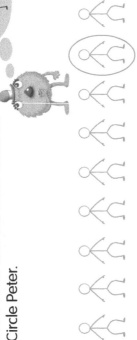

There are ___9___ children in the row.

6. Miya has some stickers.
   The stickers have the shapes below.

heart    star    flower

She arranges the stickers in this pattern:

What is the shape of the 10th sticker from the left?

 Draw the pattern to find out.

The shape of the 10th sticker from the left is a ___heart___.

## Problem Solving

1 There are four children A, B, C and D.
Read the clues.
Fill in the boxes with the correct letters.

Child A is 4th from the right.

Child C is next to Child A.

Child D is between Child C and Child B.

2 Look at these pictures.
Label them in the correct order.
Choose from these labels:

7th    4th    6th    2nd    1st
8th    3rd    9th    5th    10th

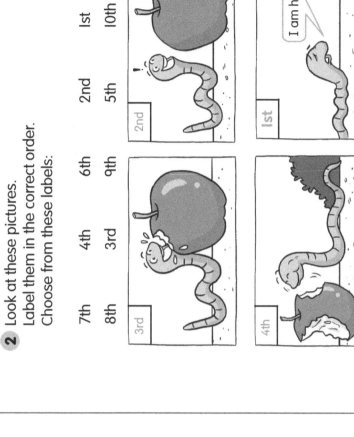

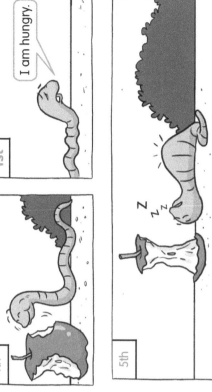

**Answers  Unit 6:** Ordinal Numbers

153

# Review 3

1. Draw the shape that comes next in the pattern.

a. ▭ ▭ ▭ ▭ ▭ ▭ | ▭

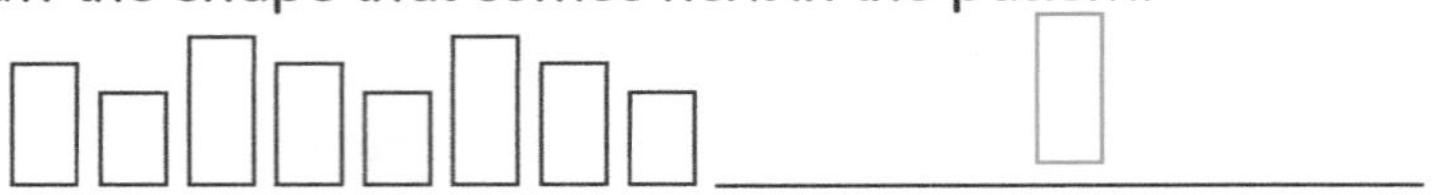

b. ◿ ◿ ◿ ◿ | ◿

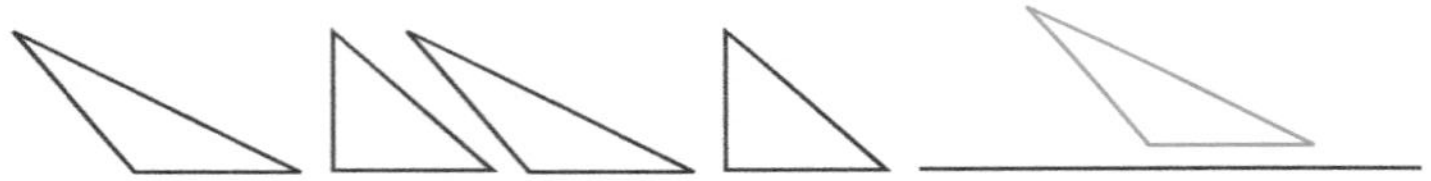

c. ▭ ○ ○ ◇ ◇ ▭ | ○ ○ | ▭

d. ▭ △ △ ▭ △ △ | ▭

e. ▭ ○ ▭ ● ○ ▭ | ○

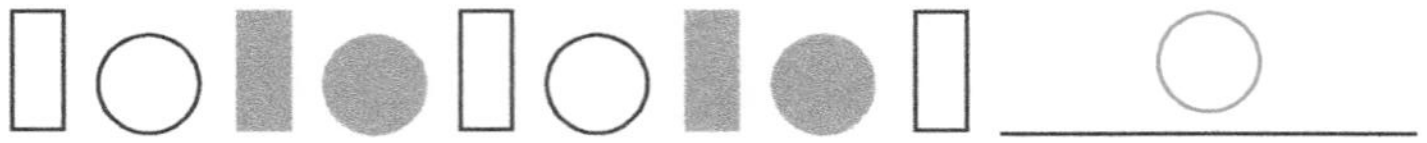

---

## Maths Journal

Write the order you think the people in Omar's family wake up in the morning.
Write what each person does when they wake up.
Use the pictures and words to help you.  Answers vary. Examples:

[ brushes her teeth ]  [ makes his bed ]  [ watches the news ]

1  **Dad is the first person to wake up.**

   **He makes breakfast.**

2  Mum is the second person to wake up. She watches the news.

3  Omar is the third person to wake up. He makes his bed.

4  Omar's sister is the fourth person to wake up. She brushes her teeth.

**3** Cross out (✗) the eighth car.

1st

**4** Cross out (✗) the 4th football from the right.

**5** Cross out (✗) the 7th pear from the left.

**6** Fill in the spaces.

Hardeep  Ella  Omar  Millie  Peter  Ruby

**a** Hardeep is ___6th / sixth___ in the queue.

**b** The ___3rd / third___ child in the queue is Millie.

**c** Peter is just after ___Ruby___.

**d** ___Omar___ is just before Ella.

**e** Ruby is ___1st / first___ in the queue.

**f** ___Omar___ is between Millie and Ella.

**g** If you want to join the queue, you should stand after ___Hardeep___.

---

**2** What comes next?
Tick (✓) the correct box.

**a**

**b**

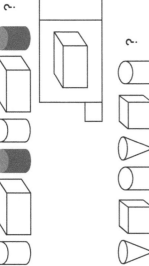

**c**

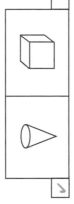 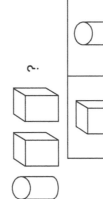

**d**

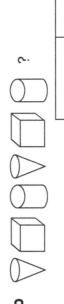

**7** This is a shape pattern.

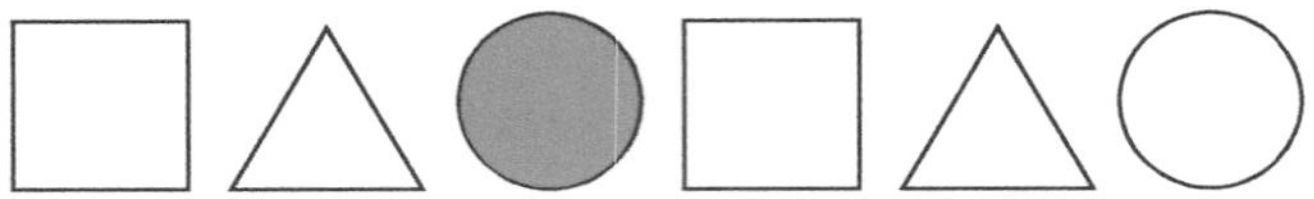

□ △ ● □ △ ○

1st

**a** Colour the 3rd shape.

**b** What is the name of the 2nd shape? ___triangle___

**c** Draw the 9th shape. ___○___

**d** Read these sentences.
Fill in the space.

The 1st shape is a square.

The 4th shape is a square.

The ___7th / seventh___ shape will also be a square.
10th / tenth
13th / thirteenth

# Unit 7: Numbers to 20

| Week | Learning Objectives | Thinking Skills | Resources |
|---|---|---|---|
| 2 | **(1) Counting to 20**<br><br>Pupils will be able to:<br>• count up to 20 by making 10 first<br>• read and write numbers 11 to 20 in numerals and words | | • Pupil Textbook IA, pp 79 to 85<br>• Practice Book IB, pp 51 to 56<br>• Teacher's Guide IA, pp 159 to 165 |
| 2 | **(2) Place value**<br><br>Pupils will be able to:<br>• represent numbers as tens and ones in a place value chart<br>• show objects in tens and ones given a number up to 20 | • Analysing parts and whole | • Pupil Textbook IA, pp 86 to 87<br>• Practice Book IB, pp 57 to 60<br>• Teacher's Guide IA, pp 166 to 167 |
| 3 | **(3) Compare**<br><br>Pupils will be able to:<br>• compare and order numbers to 20 using the terms 'greater than' and 'smaller than'<br>• compare and order numbers to 20 using the terms 'greatest' and 'smallest'<br>• compare and order numbers to 20 using the terms 'more than' and 'fewer than'<br><br>*Let's Explore!*<br><br>Pupils will be able to make number trains and understand the terms 'greatest number' and 'smallest number'. | • Comparing | • Pupil Textbook IA, pp 88 to 93<br>• Practice Book IB, pp 61 to 66<br>• Teacher's Guide IA, pp 168 to 173 |

# Unit 7: Numbers to 20

| Week | Learning Objectives | Thinking Skills | Resources |
|---|---|---|---|
| 3 | **(4) Order and pattern**<br>Pupils will be able to:<br>• compare two numbers<br>• arrange numbers in ascending or descending order | • Comparing<br>• Sequencing | • Pupil Textbook IA, pp 94 to 96<br>• Practice Book IB, pp 67 to 70<br>• Teacher's Guide IA, pp 174 to 176 |
| 3 | *Put On Your Thinking Caps!* | • Deduction<br>• Comparing<br><br>Heuristic for problem solving:<br>• Guess and check | • Pupil Textbook IA, p 97<br>• Practice Book IB, pp 71 to 74<br>• Teacher's Guide IA, pp 177 |

## Summative assessment opportunity

Assessment Book I, Test 3, pp 31 to 38

# Numbers to 20

## Learning objectives: Counting to 20

**Pupils will be able to:**

- count up to 20 by making 10 first
- read and write numbers 11 to 20 in numerals and words

## Key concept

Use one-to-one correspondence in counting.

## What you will need

20 counters such as cubes

---

**Unit 7 Numbers to 20**

**Let's Learn!**

### Counting to 20

*Counting on from 10*

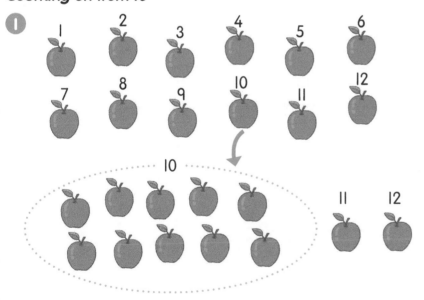

It is easier to count on: 10, **11**, 12

79

## Teaching sequence

**1**

- Take 12 counters and show pupils two different ways of counting them.
- Introduce the first method: Count all the counters starting from 1: 1, 2, 3, 4 ... 12.
- Introduce the second method: Count on from 10. First make a row of 10 counters, then count on from 10 to get 12.

## Teaching sequence

- Using the counters, count on from 10, for numbers 11 up to 20.

  **Example:**
  "10, 11"
  "10, 11, 12"
  "10, 11, 12, 13" etc.

- Point to each counter as you count.

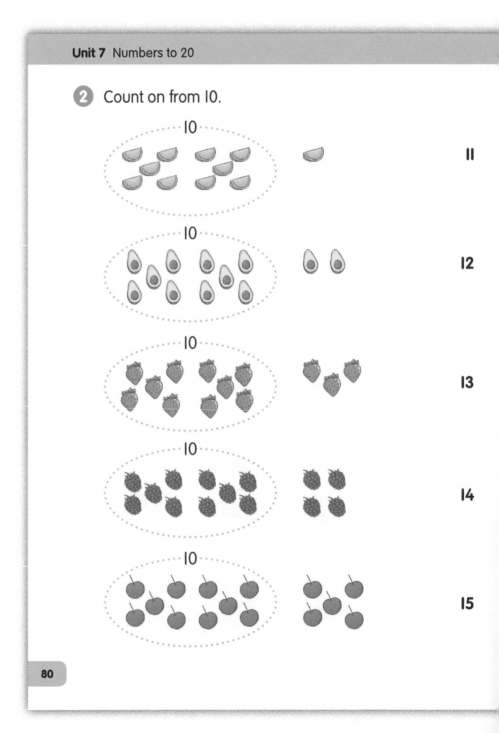

# Additional activity

Ask pupils to work in pairs. Ask one pupil to show their partner some counters (between 10 and 20). Their partner groups 10 counters to make 1 ten, and then counts from 10 to find the total number of counters. The pair then swap roles.

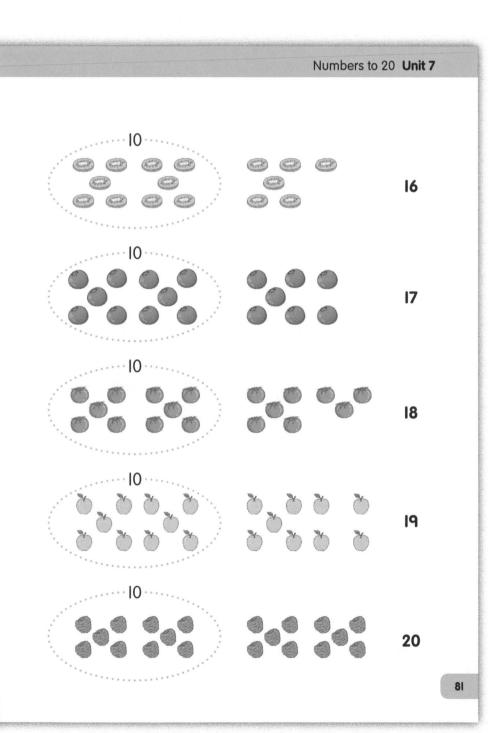

16

17

18

19

20

81

**Note**: When pupils have counted up to 20, show that there are 2 tens and use circles to show 20.

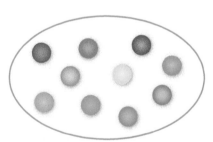

## Teaching sequence

**3** *Game*

- Model how to play the game.
- Ask pupils to work in groups of 3.
- One pupil starts counting from 1. Prompt them to show the corresponding number of fingers while counting. Remind them to count on by 1, 2 or 3.
- The rest of the pupils take turns to count aloud from the number given by the previous pupil.
- The aim is to be the first to reach '20'.
  **Example:**
  Player 1 (starts): *1, 2* (using 2 fingers)
  Player 2 (continues): *3, 4, 5* (using 3 fingers)
  Player 3 (carries on): *6, 7, 8* (using 3 fingers)
  Players continue until someone reaches 20.
- Suggest to pupils that a good strategy is to vary the number of fingers used.

# Game

Players: 3

**3** **Hit 20!**

How to play:
Take turns to count on by 1, 2 or 3. Count to 20.

1  Player 1 starts counting from 1.

2  Player 2 counts on.

3  Player 3 counts on.

The player who says 20 wins!

82

## Additional activity

Ask pupils to work in pairs. Ask one pupil to call out a number, e.g. 15. Their partner describes this number in three different ways, e.g.

(a)  10 and 5 make 15,

(b)  10 + 5 = 15,

(c)  15 is 10 and 5.

Pupils take it in turns to call out a number.

**4** First make ten.
Then count on.

10 and 4 make 14.

10 + 4 = 14

**5**

| | |
|---|---|
| **10** and **I** make **II**. | **10 + I = II** |
| **10** and **7** make I7 . | **10 + 7 =** I7 |
| **10** and **10** make 20 . | **10 + 10 =** 20 |

83

## Teaching sequence

**4** and **5**

- Introduce various ways to show numbers from 10 to 20.

  **Example:**
  Say:
  "We can express 14 in various ways:
  10 and 4 make 14,
  10 + 4 = 14."

- Ask pupils to work on the questions in the textbook together.

- Remind pupils that another way to express 14 is:
  "14 is 10 and 4."

- Link this to the number bond below.

**Additional activity**

Ask pupils to write the numbers from 10 to 20 in words. Encourage pupils who need additional support to refer to the textbook.

## Teaching sequence

- Display the poster on the board.
- Ask pupils to read the words corresponding to the numbers.
- Ask each pupil to say the words while pointing to the numbers and words.

- Ask pupils to write numbers in words from 10 to 20.

Unit 7 Numbers to 20

### *Reading number words 10 to 20*

6  Look at the number.
   Read the word.

| 10 | 11 | 12 | 13 | 14 | 15 |
|------|--------|--------|----------|----------|--------|
| ten | eleven | twelve | thirteen | fourteen | fifteen |

| 16 | 17 | 18 | 19 | 20 |
|---------|-----------|----------|----------|--------|
| sixteen | seventeen | eighteen | nineteen | twenty |

7  Give the numbers in words.

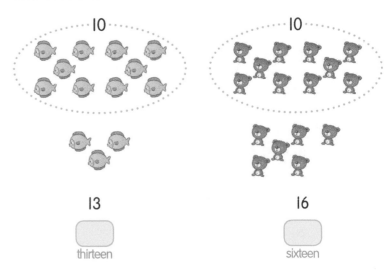

84

## Independent work

Practice I in Practice Book IB,
pp 5I to 56.

**8** Find the missing numbers.

**a**  I, 2, 3, 4, 5, 6, 7, 8, 9, [ 10 ]

**b**  10 and 4 make [ 14 ].

**c**  10 and 3 make [ 13 ].

**d**  10 and 6 make [ 16 ].

**e**  10 and 7 make [ 17 ].

**f**  10 and 9 make [ 19 ].

**g**  2 + 10 = [ 12 ]

**h**  4 + 10 = [ 14 ]

**i**  10 + 3 = [ 13 ]

**j**  10 + 8 = [ 18 ]

Practice Book IB, p.5I

85

## Teaching sequence

**8**

- Ask pupils to complete the questions and discuss their answers.

## Learning objectives: Place value

**Pupils will be able to:**

- represent numbers as tens and ones in a place value chart
- show objects in tens and ones given a number up to 20

### Key concept

Numbers to 20 can be represented as tens and ones in a place value chart.

## What you will need

- 20 counters such as drinking straws
- 2 containers or rubber bands

## Teaching sequence

- Show pupils 14 straws. Put 10 straws in a group, separate from the remaining straws, using a rubber band or container.
- Introduce pupils to the concept of 1 ten and 4 ones with the help of a place value chart. Link this to the earlier idea of '10 and 4 make 14'.

**2** and **3**

- Invite volunteers to group the counters into tens and ones and fill out the place value charts.

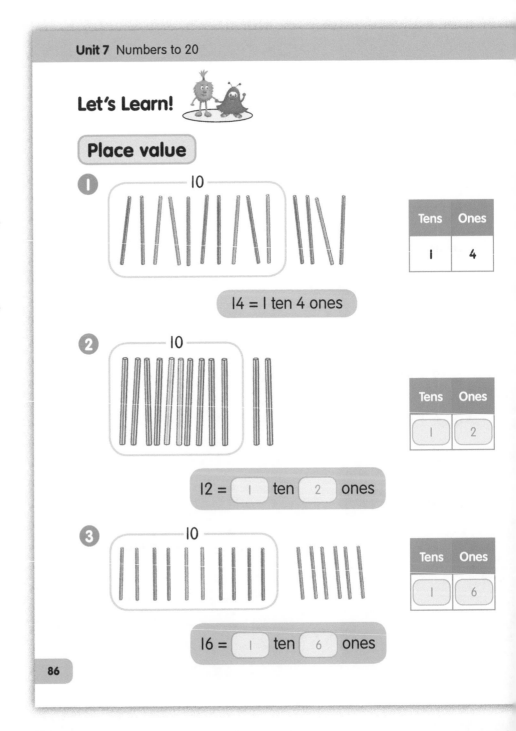

## Thinking skill

Analysing parts and whole

## What you will need

- Counters such as magnetic strips or 20 cubes
- Place value chart for each group
- 20 cubes for each group

## Independent work

Practice 2 in Practice Book IB, pp 57 to 60.

④

13 = I ten 3 ones

| Tens | Ones |
|:---:|:---:|
| I | 3 |
|  |  |

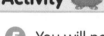

⑤ You will need a place value chart and some .

Group the  to show these numbers.

**a** 18          **b** 20

Draw ☐ for tens and □ for ones.

**Example**

place value chart

| | Tens | Ones |
|:---:|:---:|:---:|
| 15 | I | 5 |
| | ☐ | □ □<br>□ □<br>□ |

Practice Book IB, p.57

87

## Teaching sequence

④

- Show pupils 13 cubes. Fix 10 cubes to make I ten.
- Show 13 as I ten and 3 ones.
- Show the number in the place value chart.

⑤

- Arrange pupils into groups.
- Give 20 cubes to each group.
- Ask each group to show 18 and 20 with the cubes. Ask them to write the numbers and draw diagrams on the place value chart to show the numbers.
- Encourage pupils to share their place value charts and discuss their answers.

## Learning objectives: Compare

**Pupils will be able to:**

- compare and order numbers to 20 using the terms 'greater than' and 'smaller than'
- compare and order numbers to 20 using the terms 'greatest' and 'smallest'
- compare and order numbers to 20 using the terms 'more than' and 'fewer than'

## Key concept

Numbers to 20 can be compared using the terms 'greater than' and 'smaller than' as well as by arranging in ascending or descending order.

## What you will need

22 counters such as cubes

## Teaching sequence

- Group two sets of cubes. Each set should have a different number of cubes. Revise the concepts of 'more than', 'fewer than', 'how many more than', 'how many fewer than', 'greater than' and 'less than' using the sets of cubes.
- Display sets of 12 and 10 using the counters.
- Point out that there are 2 more counters in the set of 12 than the set of 10.
- Ask pupils to read and discuss the statements:
  *"12 is greater than 10."*
  *"10 is smaller than 12."*
- Work through the example in the textbook together.

---

Unit 7 Numbers to 20

## Let's Learn!

**Compare**

1. Set A

12 ⚽⚽⚽⚽⚽⚽
⚽⚽⚽⚽⚽⚽

Set B

10 ⚽⚽⚽⚽⚽
⚽⚽⚽⚽⚽

Set A has 2 more than Set B.

Set B has 2 fewer than Set A.

12 is greater than 10.

10 is smaller than 12.

88

## Thinking skill
Comparing

## What you will need
40 counters such as cubes

**2** Count the number of tennis balls in each set.

Set A | Set B
10 | 15

Which set has more balls? Set B

How many more? 5 more

Which set has fewer balls? Set A

How many fewer? 5 fewer

What is the missing number in each [ ]?

15 is greater than 10.

10 is smaller than 15.

89

## Teaching sequence
**2**

- Show pupils a set of cubes and invite volunteers to show you sets that have more or fewer cubes.
- Ask pupils to complete the questions in the textbook and discuss their answers.

## Teaching sequence

- Show the numbers 13 and 15 using the place value charts and counters.
- Explain the procedures for comparing the numbers to find out which is greater or smaller.
  **Step 1**: Compare the tens.
  **Step 2**: Compare the ones.
- Relate the concrete representation to the numbers to show which is greater.

**4** and **5**

- Ask pupils to complete the questions in the textbook.
- Explain to pupils how to align the two numbers, one below the other, for comparing to see which is greater or smaller.
  **Example:**
  $\quad$ 18
  $\quad$ 15
  Say: "*The tens are the same. 8 is greater than 5. This means 18 is greater.*"
- Invite volunteers to explain their answers using the example above for guidance.

**3** Compare 13 and 15.
Which number is greater?
How much greater is the number?

| Tens | Ones |
|------|------|
13 | 1 | 3 |

The tens are equal. This means we compare the ones.

| Tens | Ones |
|------|------|
15 | 1 | 5 |

Compare the ones. 5 is greater than 3.

15 is greater than 13 by 2.

**4** Which number is greater?
How much greater?

a $\quad$ 18 $\quad$ 15 $\quad$ 18 is greater than 15 by 3.

b $\quad$ 19 $\quad$ 17 $\quad$ 19 is greater than 17 by 2.

**5** Which number is smaller?
How much smaller?

a $\quad$ 16 $\quad$ 12 $\quad$ 12 is smaller than 16 by 4.

b $\quad$ 16 $\quad$ 13 $\quad$ 13 is smaller than 16 by 3.

90

## What you will need

Place value charts and counters such as magnetic strips or 45 cubes

## Additional activity

Repeat the Additional activity on page 170 using three numbers instead of two. Ask pupils to circle the greatest number and cross out the smallest.

**6** Compare 14, 11 and 16.

14
11
16

| | Tens | Ones |
|---|---|---|
| 14 | 1 | 4 |

The tens are all equal. This means we compare the ones.

| | Tens | Ones |
|---|---|---|
| 11 | 1 | 1 |

| | Tens | Ones |
|---|---|---|
| 16 | 1 | 6 |

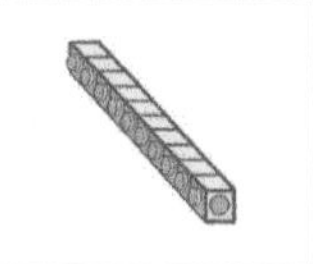

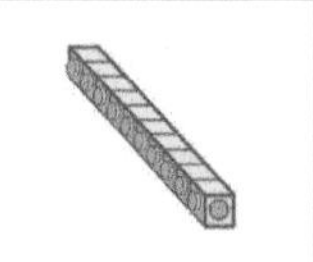

Compare the ones. 6 is greater than 4. 4 is greater than 1.

16 is the **greatest** number.
11 is the **smallest** number.

91

## Teaching sequence

**6**

- Show the numbers 14, 11 and 16 on the place value charts and arrange 14 counters, 11 counters and 16 counters as shown in the textbook.
- Point out that the picture shows that all the tens are the same. Show that 16 has the greatest number of ones and 11 has the smallest number of ones.
- Explain the procedures for comparing the numbers to find out which is the greatest or smallest.
  **Step 1**: Compare the tens.
  **Step 2**: Compare the ones.
- Relate the concrete representation on the charts to the numbers to show which is the greatest.

## Independent work

Practice 3 in Practice Book IB,
pp 61 to 66.

## Teaching sequence

- Ask pupils to complete the questions in the textbook.
- Ask pupils to align the three numbers, below each other, for comparing to see which is greatest or smallest.

  **Example:**

  10
  17
  12

  Say: "*The tens are the same. 7 is greater than 2 and 0. This means 17 is the greatest. 0 is less than 2 and 7. This means 10 is the smallest.*"

- Invite volunteers to explain their answers using the example above for guidance.

**7** Compare the numbers.
Which is the greatest?
Which is the smallest?

a 10 17 12    17, 10

b 19 14 11    19, 11

c 17 19 13    19, 13

Practice Book IB, p.61

Ask your child to compare the number of items (for example, eggs, apples, yoghurts) in your shopping trolley when you go to the supermarket.

## Objective of activity

Pupils will be able to make number trains and understand the terms 'greatest number' and 'smallest number'.

## Let's Explore!

**8**

1  Make a number train for the greatest number. Name it Train A.

2  Make a number train for the smallest number. Name it Train B.

3  How many  do you need to take from Train A and give to Train B, so that both trains have the same number of ?

Greatest number = 15

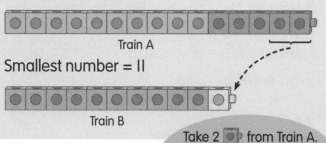

Train A

Smallest number = 11

Train B

Take 2  from Train A. Put them on Train B.

4  Now do the same thing with the following numbers:

**a**   16   11   19   19; 11; 4

**b**  20  12  17   20; 12; 4

93

## Teaching sequence

**8**  *Let's Explore!*

- Guide pupils to follow the instructions in the textbook.
- Ask pupils to explain their strategies.
- Encourage pupils to think of different ways to find the answers.
- Discuss these strategies with the class.

## Learning objectives: Order and pattern

**Pupils will be able to:**
- compare two numbers
- arrange numbers in ascending or descending order

## Key concept

Numbers can be arranged in order and made into a pattern.

## What you will need

70 cubes

## Additional activities

- Arrange a set of cubes so they do not form a pattern. Ask pupils to point out why they are not arranged in a pattern.
- Ask pupils to work in groups. Give each group 50 cubes. Ask each group to arrange two sets: one set that forms a pattern and another set that does not form a pattern. Ask each group to write down the two sets of numbers and share their results with the class.

## Teaching sequence

- Use cubes to make the pattern shown in the textbook. Explain the number pattern II, I2 ... I5 to pupils.
- Check whether pupils can see the pattern, that is: each number is greater than the number before it.
- For support, take out one cube from the next number to show the similarity and difference between the two consecutive numbers.

- Ask pupils to discuss whether the beads are arranged in a pattern.
- Ask pupils to write down the sequence of numbers.
- Ask pupils to complete the question in the textbook and discuss their answers.

---

### Let's Learn!

### Order and pattern

1 Farha uses  to make a pattern.

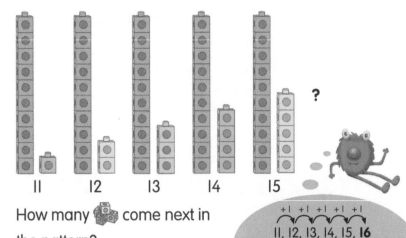

| II | I2 | I3 | I4 | I5 |

How many  come next in the pattern?

+I +I +I +I +I
II, I2, I3, I4, I5, **I6**
Each number is I more than the number before it.

2 Jack uses beads to make a pattern.

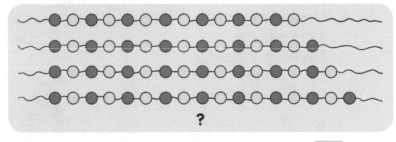

?

How many beads come next in the pattern? [ I8 ]

94

Numbers to 20 **Unit 7**

**3** Find the missing numbers.

10, 11, 12, 13, 14 , 15 , 16

13, **14**, **15**, **16**!

**4** Find the missing numbers in the number patterns.

a 14, 15, 16, 17, 18 , 19 , 20

b 20, 19, 18, 17 , 16 , 15

c 8, 10, 12, 14 , 16 , 18

d 17, 15, 13, 11 , 9 , 7

**5** What is 1 more than 15?

↓ 1 more

1 more than 15 is 16.

**6** What is 2 more than 17?

↓ 2 more

2 more than 17 is 19 .

95

Teaching sequence

**3** and **4**
- Ask pupils to complete the questions in the textbook.

**5** and **6**
- Use cubes to show that 16 is 1 more than 15 and 19 is 2 more than 17.

Ask pupils to work in groups. Ask each group to say statements similar to those in the textbook. Then ask the groups to use cubes to represent the statements to show the difference between the two numbers.

**Independent work**

Practice 4 in Practice Book IB, pp 67 to 70.

## Teaching sequence

- Demonstrate, using cubes as concrete representations, that 15 is 1 less than 16.

**8** to **10**

- Ask pupils to complete the questions in the textbook.

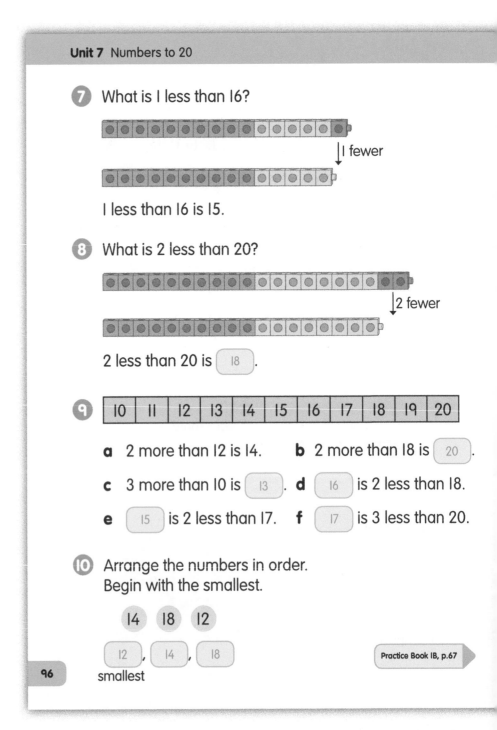

Unit 7 Numbers to 20

**7** What is 1 less than 16?

1 less than 16 is 15.

**8** What is 2 less than 20?

↓2 fewer

2 less than 20 is [ 18 ].

**9**

| 10 | 11 | 12 | 13 | 14 | 15 | 16 | 17 | 18 | 19 | 20 |

a  2 more than 12 is 14.　　b  2 more than 18 is [ 20 ].

c  3 more than 10 is [ 13 ].　d  [ 16 ] is 2 less than 18.

e  [ 15 ] is 2 less than 17.　f  [ 17 ] is 3 less than 20.

**10** Arrange the numbers in order. Begin with the smallest.

14　18　12

[ 12 ] , [ 14 ] , [ 18 ]
smallest

Practice Book IB, p.67

96

## Thinking skills

- Deduction
- Comparing

## Heuristic for problem solving

Guess and check

## What you will need

Photocopy master 15 (see page 269)

## Independent work

*Challenging Practice, Problem Solving and Maths Journal* in Practice Book 1B, pp 71 to 74.

---

# Put On Your Thinking Caps!

**a** Find the two missing numbers in the pattern. Put the cards in order.

| 10 | 14 | 16 | 20 |

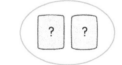

12 and 18

**b** Find the two missing numbers in the pattern. Put the cards in order.

| 12 | 14 | 15 | 16 |

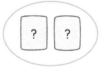

Accept 13 and 17 or 11 and 13.

There is more than one correct answer.

> Practice Book 1B, p.71 → Practice Book 1B, p.73

97

## Teaching sequence

(11) *Put On Your Thinking Caps!*

- Ask pupils to notice patterns in the numbers, and the difference between two consecutive numbers, and relate these to the problems.
- Ask pupils to guess the two missing numbers.
- Ask pupils to arrange all six numbers in order including the two numbers that they have guessed.
- Look for pupils who arrange their numbers in order to make a pattern.

**Unit 7:** Numbers to 20     **177**

Date: _____

## Practice I  Counting to 20

1 Write the correct numbers.

**Example**

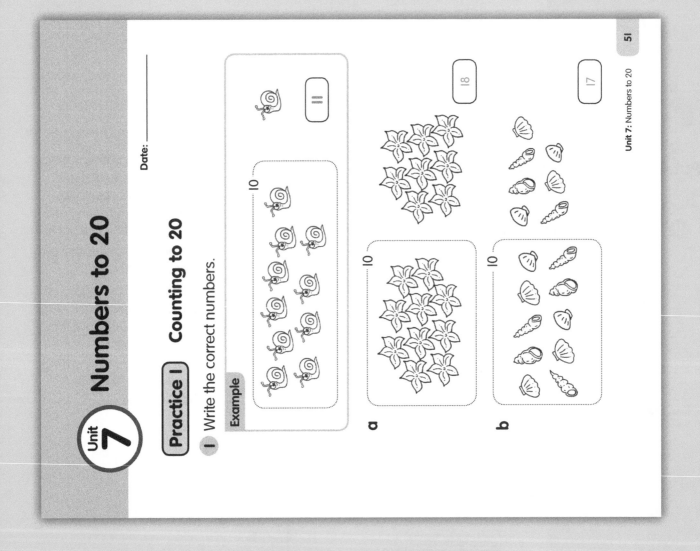

10

a   10

b   10

18

17

b
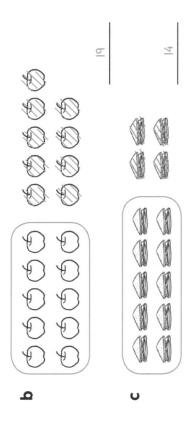

___19___

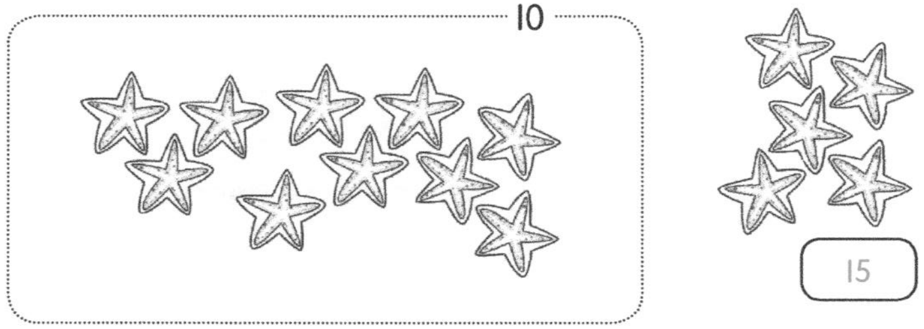

c

___14___

**3** Fill in the spaces.

a

10

10 and 8 make ___18___.

10 + 8 = ___18___

b
10

10 and 3 make ___13___.

10 + 3 = ___13___

---

c
10

___15___

d
10

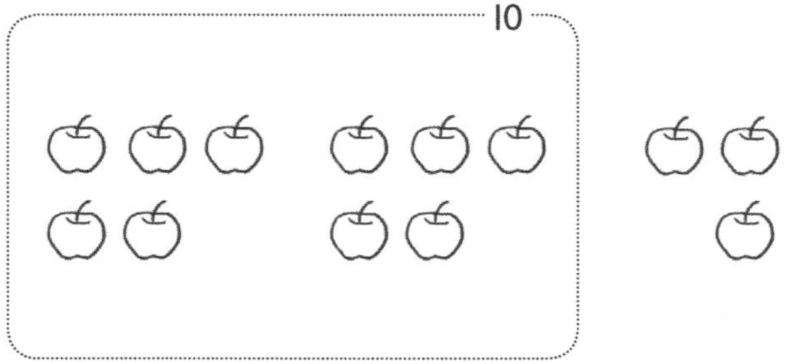

___13___

**2** Circle ten. Colour the rest. Write the total number.

**Example**
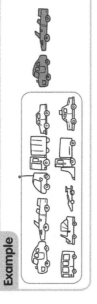
___12___

a

___16___

**5** Add the numbers.

a   $10 + 3 = \underline{13}$

b   $10 + 4 = \underline{14}$

c   $10 + 5 = \underline{15}$

d   $10 + 6 = \underline{16}$

e   $10 + 9 = \underline{19}$

f   $10 + 10 = \underline{20}$

g   $2 + 10 = \underline{12}$

h   $8 + 10 = \underline{18}$

**6** Write the correct number in words.

Example

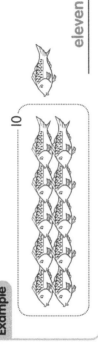

10

eleven

a

10

twelve

---

c

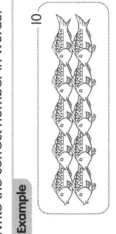

10

10 and 9 make __19__.

$10 + 9 = \underline{19}$

d

10

10 and 6 make __16__.

$10 + 6 = \underline{16}$

**4** Fill in the spaces.

a   10 and 2 make __12__.

b   10 and 5 make __15__.

c   10 and 4 make __14__.

d   10 and 7 make __17__.

Date: _____

## Practice 2  Place value

1 Look at the pictures.
Fill in the spaces.

**Example**

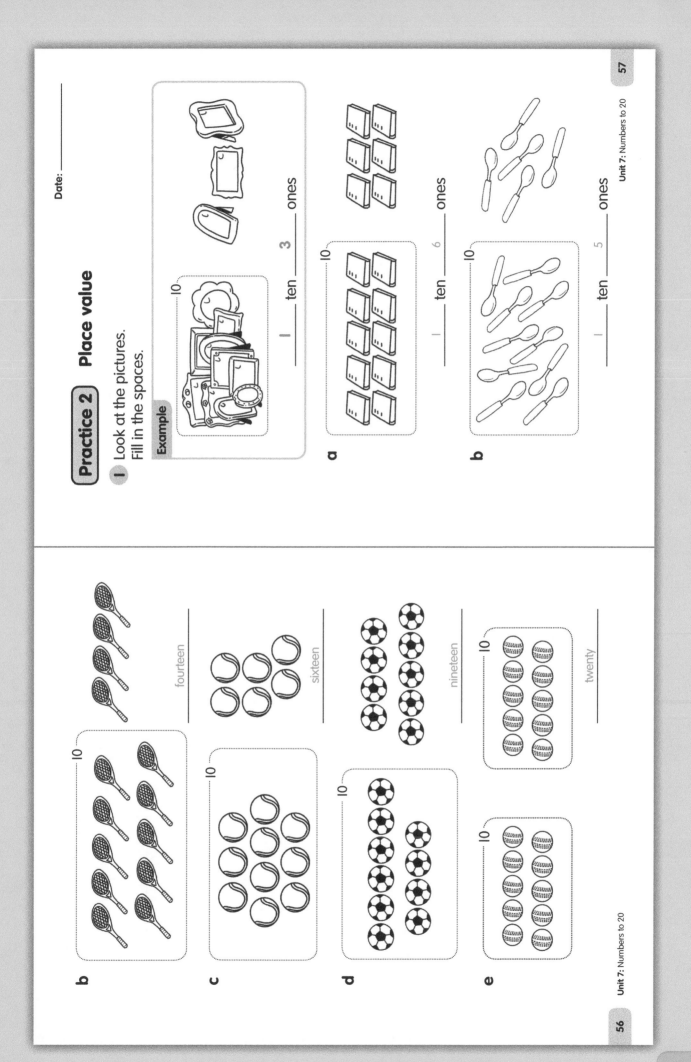

10

1 ten   3   ones

a  10

1 ten   6   ones

b  10

1 ten   5   ones

b  10

fourteen

c  10

sixteen

d  10

nineteen

e  10

twenty

## Left portion

c

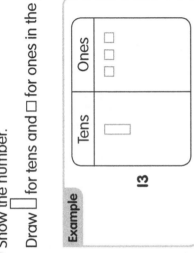

_____ 2 _____ tens _____ 0 _____ ones

**2** Fill in the place value charts.

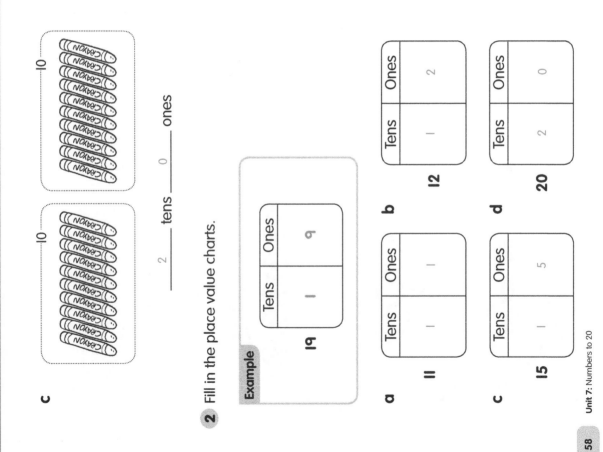

**Example**

| Tens | Ones |
|------|------|
| 1 | 9 |

19

**a**

| Tens | Ones |
|------|------|
| 1 | 1 |

11

**b**

| Tens | Ones |
|------|------|
| 1 | 2 |

12

**c**

| Tens | Ones |
|------|------|
| 1 | 5 |

15

**d**

| Tens | Ones |
|------|------|
| 2 | 0 |

20

## Right portion

**3** Show the number.

Draw ⬜ for tens and □ for ones in the place value charts.

**Example**

| Tens | Ones |
|------|------|
| | □ □ □ |

13

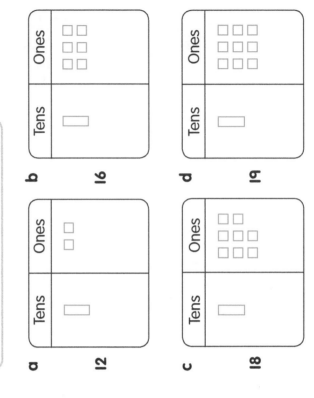

**a**

| Tens | Ones |
|------|------|
| | □ □ |

12

**b**

| Tens | Ones |
|------|------|
| | □ □ □ □ □ □ |

16

**c**

| Tens | Ones |
|------|------|
| | □ □ □ □ □ □ □ □ |

18

**d**

| Tens | Ones |
|------|------|
| | □ □ □ □ □ □ □ □ □ |

19

Date: _____

## Practice 3  Compare

**1** Which set has more? How many more?

**a**
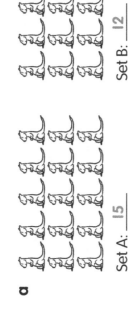

Set A: __15__    Set B: __12__

Set __A__ has __3__ more kangaroos than Set __B__.

**b**
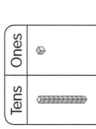

Set A: __14__    Set B: __18__

Set __B__ has __4__ more penguins than Set __A__.

**c**
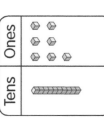
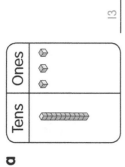

Set A: __19__    Set B: __11__

Set __A__ has __8__ more birds than Set __B__.

---

**4** Look at the place value charts.
Write the numbers shown.

**a**

| Tens | Ones |
|------|------|
| ▭ | ⬡ ⬡ ⬡ |

__13__

**b**

| Tens | Ones |
|------|------|
| ▭ | ⬡ ⬡ ⬡ ⬡ ⬡ ⬡ ⬡ |

__17__

**c**

| Tens | Ones |
|------|------|
| ▭ | ⬡ ⬡ ⬡ ⬡ |

__14__

**d**

| Tens | Ones |
|------|------|
| ▭ | ⬡ |

__11__

**5** Fill in the spaces.

**a** 13 = 1 ten __3__ ones

**b** 17 = __1__ ten 7 ones

**c** 15 = 1 ten __5__ ones

**d** 12 = __1__ ten 2 ones

**e** 19 = 1 ten __9__ ones

**3** Colour the house with the smaller number.
Fill in the spaces.

**Example**

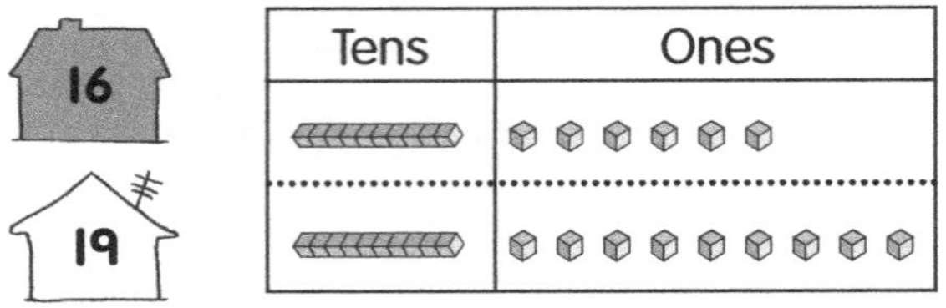

| Tens | Ones |
|---|---|
|  |  |

16

19

19 is greater than 16

16 is smaller than 19 .

The tens are equal.
Compare the ones.
9 ones is greater than 6 ones.
6 ones is smaller than 9 ones.

**a**

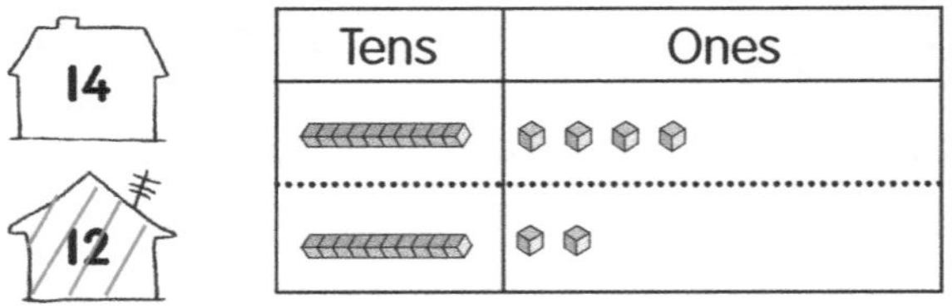

| Tens | Ones |
|---|---|
|  |  |

14

12

12 is smaller than 14

**b**

| Tens | Ones |
|---|---|
|  |  |

19

17

19 is greater than 17 .

**2** Which set has fewer? How many fewer?

**a**

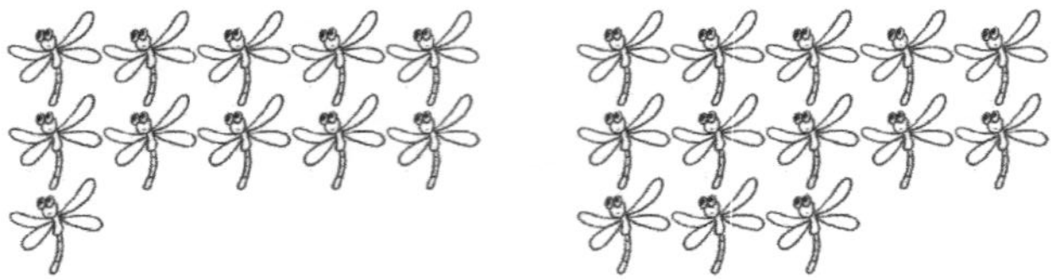

Set A: 11    Set B: 13

Set A has 2 fewer dragonflies than Set B .

**b**

Set A: 19    Set B: 17

Set B has 2 fewer butterflies than Set A .

**c**

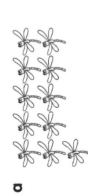

Set A: 16    Set B: 12

Set B has 4 fewer bees than Set A .

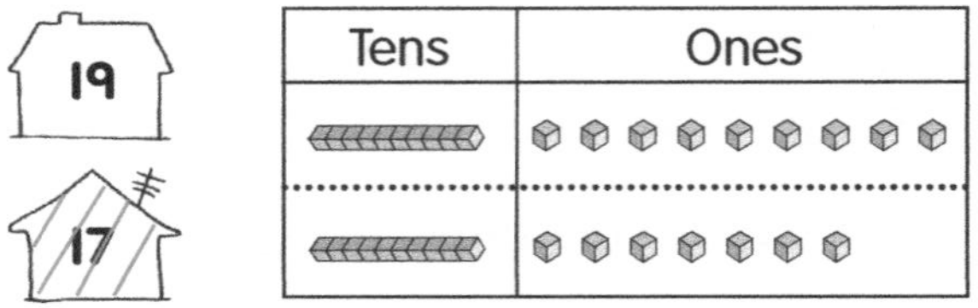

**4** Colour the animal with the smaller number in red.
Colour the animal with the greater number in blue.

**a**

blue 17    red 15

**b**

red 18    blue 19

**5 a** Colour the toy with the greater number.

How much greater is the number? ___3___

**b** Colour the toy with the smaller number.

How much smaller is the number? ___4___

---

**6** Fill in the spaces in the place value charts.

**a** Colour the sign with the greatest number.

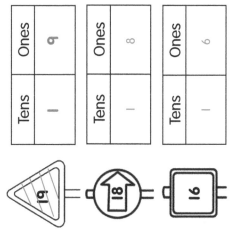

| Tens | Ones |
|------|------|
| 1 | 9 |

| Tens | Ones |
|------|------|
| 1 | 8 |

| Tens | Ones |
|------|------|
| 1 | 6 |

**b** Colour the sign with the smallest number.

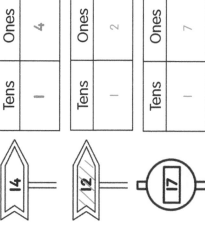

| Tens | Ones |
|------|------|
| 1 | 4 |

| Tens | Ones |
|------|------|
| 1 | 2 |

| Tens | Ones |
|------|------|
| 1 | 7 |

## Practice 4 Order and pattern

1. Tai uses stars to make a pattern.
How many stars come next in the pattern?
Draw the stars in the empty box.
Write the number of stars below the box.

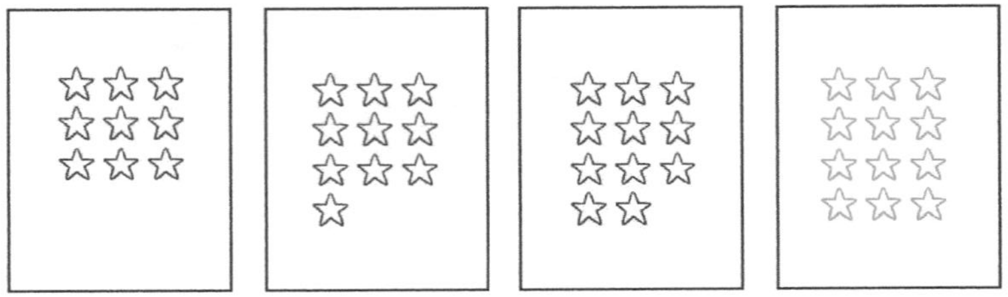

☆☆☆ ☆☆☆ ☆☆☆    ☆☆☆ ☆☆☆ ☆☆☆    ☆☆☆ ☆☆☆ ☆☆☆    ☆☆☆ ☆☆☆ ☆☆☆

___12___

2. Find the missing numbers.

a  12  13  14  15  16  17

b 15  16  17  18  19  20

c 14  13  12  11  10  9

---

7. Compare the numbers.
Fill in the spaces.

a  17  18  12

__12__ is the smallest number.

__18__ is the greatest number.

b  13  16  15  10

__10__ is the smallest number.

__16__ is the greatest number.

c  19  9  18  14  11

__9__ is the smallest number.

__19__ is the greatest number.

## 4 Complete the number patterns.

a [10] [11] [12] [13] [14]

b [19] [18] [17] [16] [19]

c [9] [11] [13] [15] [17]

d [12] [14] [16] [18] [20]

e [19] [17] [15] [13] [11]

f [11] [13] [15] [17] [19]

g [14] [12] [10] [8] [6] [4] [2]

h [8] [11] [14] [17] [20]

---

## 3 Look at the numbers.

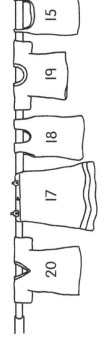

20   17   18   19   15

Fill in the spaces.

a _17_ is 2 more than 15.

b _18_ is 2 less than 20.

c 1 more than 18 is _19_.

d 2 less than 19 is _17_.

e _20_ is the greatest number.

f _15_ is the smallest number.

Date: _____

**Challenging Practice**

1. Omar, Miya, Peter, Tai and Hardeep make sandwiches for a school fair. Who makes the most sandwiches?

**Clues**

- Hardeep makes the fewest sandwiches.
- Miya makes 3 more sandwiches than Hardeep.
- Tai makes more than Miya but fewer than Omar.

Write the correct names next to the sandwiches.

| Name | Sandwiches |
| --- | --- |
| Peter | |
| Tai | |
| Omar | |
| Hardeep | |
| Miya | |

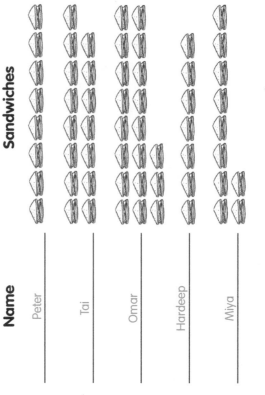

Who makes the most sandwiches? __Omar__

---

5. These are Ella's toys.
Help her arrange the cars and trucks.

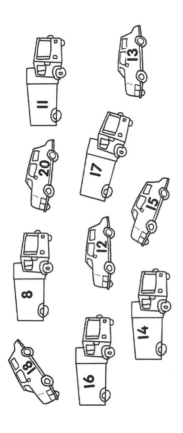

**a** Write the numbers on the  in order.
Begin with the smallest number.

smallest

12   13   15   18   20

**b** Write the numbers on the  in order.
Begin with the greatest number.

greatest

17   16   14   11   8

## Problem Solving

**1**

Read what Peter's friends say.
Circle the numbers that were covered.

First cover the greatest number on your card.

Next cover the number that is 2 less than the greatest number.

Then cover the number that is the smallest.

There are two more numbers. One of these numbers is 3 less than the other.

| | | | |
|---|---|---|---|
| (1) | 9 | 13 | (18) |
| 5 | 3 | 7 | 17 |
| (16) | 11 | (15) | (12) |

---

**2** Fill in the spaces.

a   $10 + \underline{5} = 15$

b   $10 + \underline{1} = 11$

c   $10 + \underline{8} = 18$

d   $\underline{4} + 10 = 14$

e   $\underline{7} + 10 = 17$

f   $10 + \underline{9} = 19$

**3** These are the numbers of 12 children taking part in a quiz.

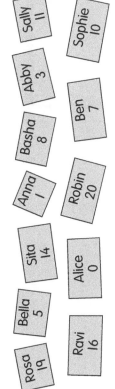

Rosa 19   Bella 5   Sita 14   Anna 1   Basha 8   Abby 3   Sally 11

Alice 0   Ravi 16   Robin 20   Ben 7   Sophie 10

Write the names of the children in the correct boxes.

| Numbers less than 5 | Numbers from 5 to 9 | Numbers from 10 to 14 | Numbers from 15 to 20 |
|---|---|---|---|
| Anna<br>Alice<br>Abby | Bella<br>Basha<br>Ben | Sita<br>Sally<br>Sophie | Ravi<br>Rosa<br>Robin |

What do you spot about the names of the children in each group?

They start with the same letter.

Date: _____

## Maths Journal

Look at the picture.

Hardeep

Ella

Miya

Peter

1 Write about the number of stickers the friends have.
Use **more than, fewer than, the greatest number** and
**the smallest number.**

a    **Miya has more stickers than Ella.**

b    Answers vary _____

c    _____

d    _____

2 Make a number pattern using the number of stickers.

4, 7, 10, 13 or 13, 10, 7, 4 _____

# Unit 8: Addition and Subtraction within 20

| Week | Learning Objectives | Thinking Skills | Resources |
|------|---------------------|-----------------|-----------|
| 4 | **(1) Ways to add**<br><br>Pupils will be able to:<br>• add two 1-digit numbers using the 'make 10' strategy<br>• add one 1-digit number and one 2-digit number using the 'regrouping into tens and ones' strategy | • Analysing parts and whole | • Pupil Textbook IA, pp 98 to 101<br>• Practice Book IB, pp 75 to 80<br>• Teacher's Guide IA, pp 194 to 197 |
| 4 | **(2) Ways to subtract**<br><br>Pupils will be able to:<br>• subtract a 1-digit number from a 2-digit number when regrouping is not required<br>• subtract a 1-digit number from a 2-digit number when regrouping is required | • Analysing parts and whole | • Pupil Textbook IA, pp 102 to 105<br>• Practice Book IB, pp 81 to 88<br>• Teacher's Guide IA, pp 198 to 201 |

# Unit 8: Addition and Subtraction within 20

| Week | Learning Objectives | Thinking Skills | Resources |
|---|---|---|---|
| 5 | **(3) Solving word problems**<br><br>Pupils will be able to:<br>• solve one-step word problems using the 'part-whole' or 'adding on' concepts in addition<br>• solve one-step word problems using the 'part-whole' or 'taking away' concepts in subtraction<br><br>*Maths Journal*<br><br>Pupils will be able to reflect on the addition and/or subtraction concepts, write a story and solve the problem.<br><br>*Let's Explore!*<br><br>Pupils will be able to find out the different combinations of numbers in addition and subtraction from a given set of numbers. | • Analysing parts and whole | • Pupil Textbook IA, pp I06 to I07<br>• Practice Book IB, pp 89 to 90<br>• Teacher's Guide IA, pp 202 to 203 |

# Unit 8: Addition and Subtraction within 20

| Week | Learning Objectives | Thinking Skills | Resources |
|------|--------------------|-----------------|-----------|
| 5 | *Put On Your Thinking Caps!*<br><br>Pupils will be able to recall addition and subtraction number bonds for numbers to 20 to solve problems. | • Analysing parts and whole | • Pupil Textbook IA, pp 108 to 109<br>• Practice Book IB, pp 91 to 94<br>• Teacher's Guide IA, pp 204 to 205 |

# Addition and Subtraction within 20

**Learning objectives:**
**Ways to add**

**Pupils will be able to:**

- add two 1-digit numbers using the 'make 10' strategy
- add one 1-digit number and one 2-digit number using the 'regrouping into tens and ones' strategy

**Key concept**

Two 1-digit numbers can be added by using the 'make 10' strategy and the 'regrouping into tens and ones' strategy.

## Teaching sequence

- Show pupils a group of 8 red cubes and a group of 6 yellow cubes. Explain that you are going to add the cubes.
- Remove 2 cubes from the yellow group and put them in the red group to make 10 cubes. Ask pupils to count the number of tens and ones.
- Write the following number bond 6—2-4 and addition sentence '8 + 6 = 10 + 4 = 14' on the board.
- Emphasise to pupils that they should make 10 first when adding.
- Revise the number bonds for 10 if necessary.
- Using the cubes, demonstrate the addition of other 1-digit numbers within 20 using same strategy.

---

Unit **8** Addition and Subtraction within 20

**Let's Learn!**

**Ways to add**

*Adding by making 10*

1. Peter has 8 cherries. Ruby gives him 6 more.

How many cherries does Peter have now?

$8 + 6 = ?$

$$8 \quad + \quad 6$$

$$10 \qquad 4$$

First make a group of 10 cherries.

Then add the cherries that are left over.
$10 + 4 = 14$

Peter has 14 cherries now.

$$8 + 6 = 10 + 4$$
$$= 14$$

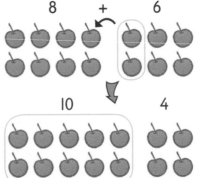

2    4

98

**Thinking skill**
Analysing parts and whole

**What you will need**
- 20 cubes or counters in two colours (e.g. red and yellow)
- 20 drinking straws in two colours for each group

**Teaching sequence**

**2**

- Ask pupils to work in groups. Give pupils drinking straws. Ask each group to show and apply the 'make 10' strategy in various addition situations.

  **Examples**:
  $9 + 2$
  $7 + 4$
  $8 + 5$

- Ask pupils to complete the questions in the textbook and discuss their answers.

Addition and Subtraction within 20 **Unit 8**

## Activity

**2** Group the straws to make 10.
Then find the answer.

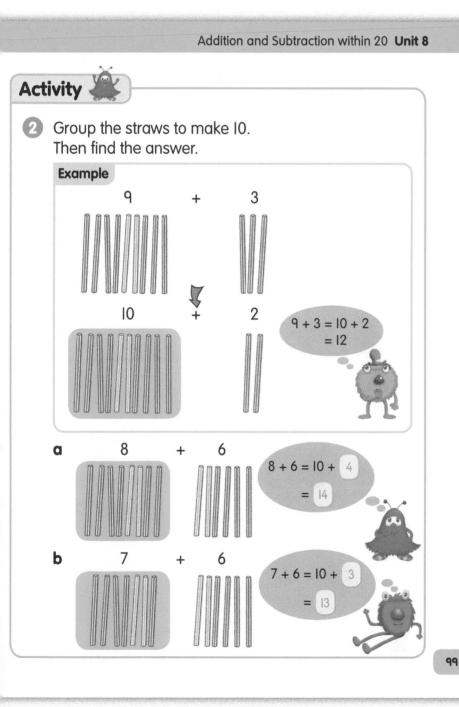

**Example**

9 + 3

10 + 2

$9 + 3 = 10 + 2$
$= 12$

**a** 8 + 6

$8 + 6 = 10 + \boxed{4}$
$= \boxed{14}$

**b** 7 + 6

$7 + 6 = 10 + \boxed{3}$
$= \boxed{13}$

99

## Teaching sequence

- Show pupils how to use cubes for regrouping using the 'make 10' strategy.
- Ask pupils to work through the example then the problems, using cubes for support.

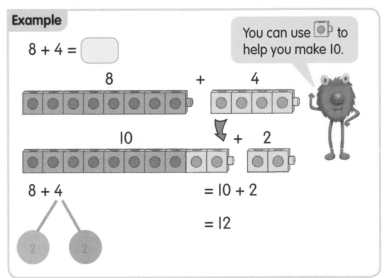

**Unit 8** Addition and Subtraction within 20

③ Add by making 10.

**Example**

$8 + 4 = \boxed{\phantom{0}}$

You can use 🔲 to help you make 10.

8 + 4

$8 + 4$
$= 10 + 2$
$= 12$

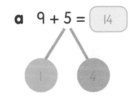 **a** $9 + 5 = \boxed{14}$

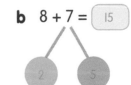 **b** $8 + 7 = \boxed{15}$

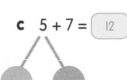 **c** $5 + 7 = \boxed{12}$

We break the smaller number into 2 parts.

100 | 🏠 Home Maths | Help your child to practise adding by making 10 using objects around the house such as beads, buttons or paper clips. | **Practice Book 1B, p.75**

## *Adding by regrouping into tens and ones*

**4** Tai has 16 blue marbles.
His sister gives him 3 yellow marbles.

Step 1    16   + 3    Regroup 16 into 10 and ones.

Step 2    Add 3 to 6.
6 + 3 = 9    Add the ones.

Step 3    10 + 9 = 19

16 + 3 = 19

Tai has 19 marbles altogether.

**5** Regroup the numbers into tens and ones.
Then add the numbers.

**a** 13 + 3 = 16

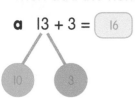

**b** 12 + 7 = 19

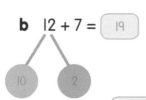

Practice Book 1B, p.79

101

## Teaching sequence

**4**

- Show pupils two different types of problem:
  9 + 5 and 12 + 7
- Ask pupils if they can notice the difference between the two problems and what the differences are.
- Encourage pupils to recall the place values of the number 16 and show the number bond for
  16: 16—10-6. Say:
  *"16 is 1 ten and 6 ones."*
- Model the three steps in the textbook.
- Invite volunteers to show and apply the 'regrouping into tens and ones' strategy in various addition situations. Give volunteers counters or cubes.
  **Examples**:
  13 + 5,   14 + 5.

**5**

- Ask pupils to complete the questions in the textbook.

Learning objectives:
## Ways to subtract

**Pupils will be able to:**

- subtract a 1-digit number from a 2-digit number when regrouping is not required
- subtract a 1-digit number from a 2-digit number when regrouping is required

## Key concept

2-digit numbers can be regrouped into tens and ones.

## Teaching sequence

- Revise briefly the 'taking away' strategy of subtraction and relate this strategy to the word problem in the textbook: 17 – 3, i.e., taking 3 away from 17.
- Encourage pupils to recall the place values of the number 17 and show the number bond for 17: 17—10-7. Say:

  *"17 is 1 ten and 7 ones."*
- Model the three steps in the textbook.

---

**Unit 8** Addition and Subtraction within 20

### Let's Learn!

**Ways to subtract**

#### *Subtracting by regrouping into tens and ones*

1. Peter has 17 toy cars.
   He gives away 3 toy cars.

| Step 1 | | Regroup 17 into 10 and ones. |
|--------|--|------------------------------|

17 – 3

10    7

Regroup 17 into 10 and ones.
17 = 10 + 7

**Step 2**   Subtract 3 from 7.
7 – 3 = 4

Subtract the ones.

**Step 3**   10 + 4 = 14

17 – 3 = 14

Peter has 14 toy cars left.

## Thinking skill
Analysing parts and whole

## What you will need
30 counters such as cubes or
drinking straws for each group

**2** Regroup the numbers into tens and ones.
Then subtract the numbers.

**a** $17 - 5 =$ 12

**b** $18 - 3 =$ 15

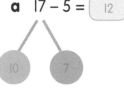

**3** Where is Big Ben?
Subtract to find out.

13 − 3 = 10 **N**    17 − 6 =  **O**

16 − 2 = 14 **D**    18 − 5 = 13 **N**

16 − 1 = 15 **O**    19 − 3 = 16 **L**

| L | O | N | D | O | N |
|---|---|---|---|---|---|
| 16 | 11 | 10 | 14 | 15 | 13 |

## Teaching sequence

**2**

- Invite volunteers to solve the following with cubes:
  17 − 5 and 18 − 3
- Encourage pupils to use the following steps:
  1) Group a 2-digit number into tens and ones.
  2) Take away the 1-digit number from the ones.
  3) Show the result.

**3**

- Ask pupils to work in groups. Give each group counters such as cubes or drinking straws.
- Ask pupils to complete the question.

## Note

For more able pupils, you could introduce the following number bond to answer question **4**.

## Additional activity

Invite volunteers to show and apply the 'regrouping into tens and ones' strategy to various subtraction situations. Give pupils drinking straws or cubes.
**Examples**:

13 – 7 and 14 – 9

Encourage pupils to explain the procedures they used in subtraction.

## Teaching sequence

- Show two different types of problems:
  17 – 3 and 12 – 7.
- Ask pupils if they can see the differences between the problems and what the differences are.
- Encourage pupils to recall the place values of the number 12 and show the number bond for 12.
  Say:
  *"12 is 1 ten and 2 ones."*
- Model the steps in the textbook using the number bond and 'regrouping into tens and ones' strategy.
- Explain why 10 is placed after 2 in the number bond.

- Ask pupils to complete the questions.

---

### More subtraction

**4** Hardeep makes 12 stars.
He gives 7 stars to Ella.

Step 1    12 – 7

Regroup 12 into 10 and ones.
12 = 10 + 2

Step 2   10 – 7 = 3

We cannot subtract 7 from 2.
We subtract 7 from 10.

Step 3   2 + 3 = 5

12 – 7 = 5

Hardeep has 5 stars left.

**5** Subtract the numbers.

a   11 – 3 = [ 8 ]

b   13 – 6 = [ 7 ]

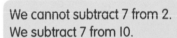

**Addition and Subtraction within 20  Unit 8**

## Game

### 6 Spin and subtract!

How to play:

A

B

Players: 3
You will need:
• Spinners A and B

**1** Use both spinners to get 2 numbers.

**2** The other 2 players subtract the Spinner B number from the Spinner A number.

**3** The first player with the correct answer wins 1 point. Take turns to spin.

Play six rounds. The player with the most points wins!

Practice Book 1B, p.81

105

### Teaching sequence

**6** *Game*

• Ask pupils to work in groups of 3.

• Guide pupils through the instructions to find two numbers and to work out the answer.

**Pupils will be able to:**

- solve one-step word problems using the 'part-whole' or 'adding on' concepts in addition

- solve one-step word problems using the 'part-whole' or 'taking away' concepts in subtraction

## Key concept

Applying the 'part-whole', 'adding on' and 'taking away' concepts in addition and subtraction

## Teaching sequence

- Ask pupils to look at the picture and sentences from the word problem.
- Explain the 'adding on' concept required in this problem and illustrate it with cubes.
- Write the addition sentence on the board.

- Look for pupils who can solve the word problem by relating groups in the sentences.

- Look for pupils who can solve the word problem by relating sentences to the 'taking away' concept.

---

**Unit 8** Addition and Subtraction within 20

## Let's Learn!

### Solving word problems

1. Ruby has 9 🔲.
   Farha gives her 6 🔲.
   How many 🎲 does Ruby have altogether?

   9 + 6 = 15

   Ruby has 15 🎲 altogether.

2. Omar has 3 counters.
   Millie has 14 counters.
   How many counters do they have altogether? 17 counters

3. Jack has 16 shells.
   He gives Miya 5 shells.
   How many shells does Jack have left?

   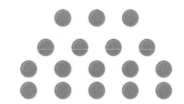

   16 – 5 = 11

   Jack has 11 shells left.

## Objectives of activities

**Pupils will be able to:**

- reflect on the addition and/or subtraction concepts
- write a story and solve the problem
- find out the different combinations of numbers in addition and subtraction from a given set of numbers

## Thinking skill

Analysing parts and whole

## What you will need

Photocopy master 16 (see page 270)

## Independent work

Practice 4 in Practice Book IB, pp 89 to 90.

---

**4** Hardeep has 11 paper clips.
3 of them are blue.
The rest are red.
How many red paper clips are there?

8 red paper clips

Practice Book IB, p.89

## Maths Journal

**5** Look at the children around you.

Write an addition story about them.

Write a subtraction story about them.

## Let's Explore!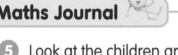

**6** Make up number sentences using the following numbers. Use addition and subtraction.

You can use each number more than once.

 5  6  7  8  9  13 15

How many families of number sentences can you make? 4

7 + 6 = 13, 6 + 7 = 13, 13 − 6 = 7, 13 − 7 = 6
8 + 7 = 15, 7 + 8 = 15, 15 − 7 = 8, 15 − 8 = 7
8 + 5 = 13, 5 + 8 = 13, 13 − 5 = 8, 13 − 8 = 5
9 + 6 = 15, 6 + 9 = 15, 15 − 6 = 9, 15 − 9 = 6

107

## Teaching sequence

**4**

Look for pupils who can relate the statements to the 'part-whole' concept.

**5** *Maths Journal*

- Ask pupils to write a story using the following concepts: 'part-whole', 'adding on' and 'taking away'. Ask pupils to use numbers within 20.
- Provide examples for pupils who need additional support.

**6** *Let's Explore!*

- Ask pupils to investigate all possible number sentences using addition and subtraction. Encourage them to recall number bonds.

## Objective of activity

Pupils will be able to recall addition and subtraction number bonds for numbers to 20 to solve problems.

## Thinking skill

Analysing parts and whole

## What you will need

Photocopy master 17 (see page 271)

## Teaching sequence

**7** *Put On Your Thinking Caps!*

- Ask pupils to work on the problem. Explain to pupils that these problems involve the use of number bonds in addition.
- Look for pupils who notice that 15 is the largest number and it should be placed in the orange circle.
- Pupils will need to make number bonds with 15, 9 and 8 as the total.

## Put On Your Thinking Caps!

**7** Use all these numbers to solve the puzzle. Use each number once.

3   4   5   6   7   15

➜ and ⬇ mean =.

(Hint: The number in the ⚙ is the greatest.)

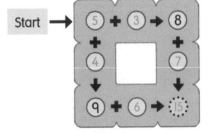

108

## Independent work

*Challenging Practice* and
*Problem Solving* in Practice Book
IB, pp 91 to 94.

# Put On Your Thinking Caps!

8 Use all these numbers to solve the puzzle.
Use each number once.

3    4    6    7    8    17

→ and ↓ mean =.

(Hint: The number in the ⚙ is the greatest.)

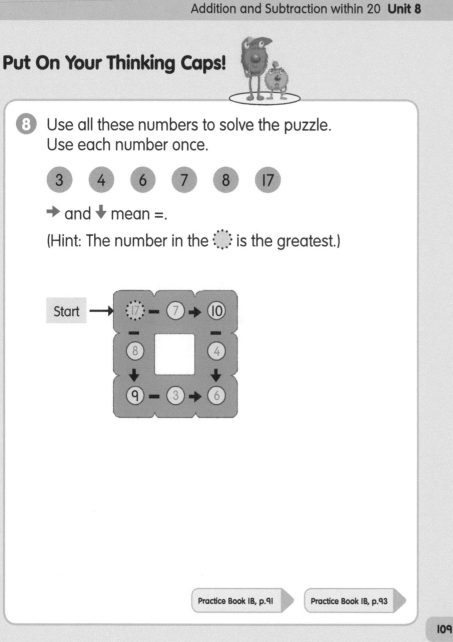

Start →

Practice Book IB, p.91    Practice Book IB, p.93

109

## Teaching sequence

8 *Put On Your Thinking Caps!*

• Look for pupils who notice that
as 17 is the largest number,
they need to place it in the
orange circle.

• Another clue in this question
is that numbers 9 and 10 are
given. Therefore, number
bonds for 9 and 10 are
needed.

# Unit 8 Addition and Subtraction within 20

Date: _____

**Practice 1    Ways to add**

1 Circle the objects to make 10.
Then add the ones.

**Example**

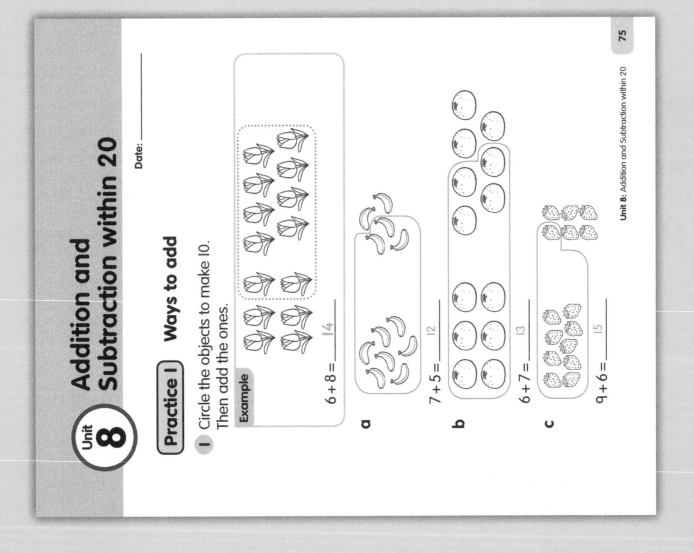

6 + 8 = 14

**a**    7 + 5 = 12

**b**    6 + 7 = 13

**c**    9 + 6 = 15

**2** Complete the addition sentences.

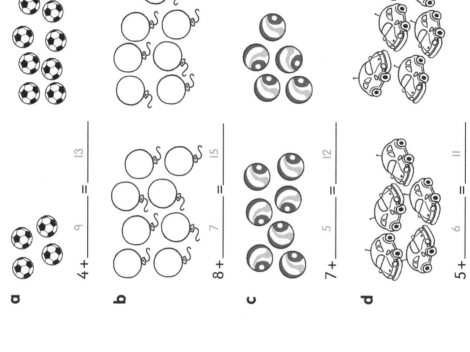

**a**

$4 + 9 = 13$

**b**

$8 + 7 = 15$

**c**

$7 + 5 = 12$

**d**

$5 + 6 = 11$

---

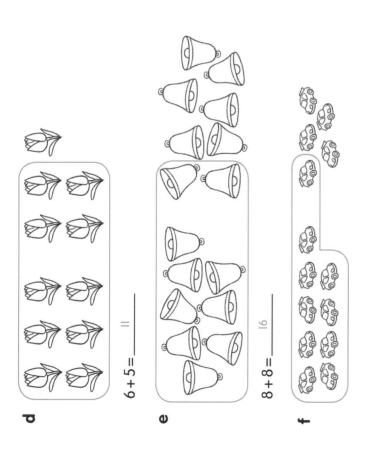

**d**

$6 + 5 = 11$

**e**

$8 + 8 = 16$

**f**

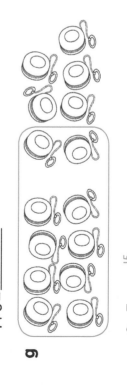

**g**

$9 + 5 = 14$

$8 + 7 = 15$

**Answers  Unit 8:** Addition and Subtraction within 20   **207**

## Practice 2 Ways to add

**1** Regroup the numbers into tens and ones.
Then add the numbers.

**Example**

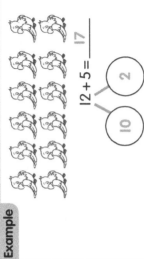

$12 + 5 = 17$

(10, 2)

**a**

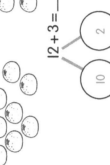

$12 + 3 = 15$

(10, 2)

**b**

$11 + 5 = 16$

(10, 1)

---

**3** Fill in the number bonds.
Add by making 10.

**Example**

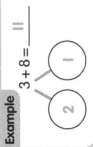

$3 + 8 = 11$

(2, 1)

$8 + 2 = 10$

$10 + 1 = 11$

**a**   $5 + 9 = 14$

(4, 1)

$9 + 1 = 10$

$10 + 4 = 14$

**b**   $6 + 6 = 12$

(4, 2)

$6 + 4 = 10$

$10 + 2 = 12$

**c**   $7 + 8 = 15$

(5, 2)

$8 + 2 = 10$

$10 + 5 = 15$

**d**   $9 + 9 = 18$

(8, 1)

$9 + 1 = 10$

$10 + 8 = 18$

## Practice 3  Ways to subtract

1  Regroup the numbers into tens and ones. Then subtract the numbers.

Example

$13 - 2 = 11$

10    3

a        $14 - 1 = 13$

10    4

b    $17 - 3 = 14$

10    7

c    $18 - 6 = 12$

10    8

c    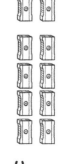    $14 + 3 = 17$

10    4

d        $8 + 11 = 19$

10    1

2  Add the numbers.

a  $15 + 2 = 17$    b  $12 + 4 = 16$

c  $13 + 5 = 18$    d  $6 + 11 = 17$

e  $7 + 12 = 19$    f  $9 + 11 = 20$

## 2 Regroup the numbers into tens and ones. Then subtract the numbers.

**Example**

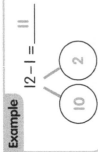

$12 - 1 = \underline{11}$

$2 - 1 = \underline{1}$

$10 + 1 = \underline{11}$

**a** $14 - 2 = \underline{12}$

10 | 4

$4 - 2 = \underline{2}$

$10 + 2 = \underline{12}$

**b** $15 - 3 = \underline{12}$

10 | 5

$5 - 3 = \underline{2}$

$10 + 2 = \underline{12}$

**c** $16 - 3 = \underline{13}$

10 | 6

$6 - 3 = \underline{3}$

$10 + 3 = \underline{13}$

**d** $19 - 3 = \underline{16}$

10 | 9

$9 - 3 = \underline{6}$

$10 + 6 = \underline{16}$

**e** $16 - 4 = \underline{12}$

10 | 6

$6 - 4 = \underline{2}$

$10 + 2 = \underline{12}$

**f** $18 - 4 = \underline{14}$

10 | 8

$8 - 4 = \underline{4}$

$10 + 4 = \underline{14}$

**g** $19 - 5 = \underline{14}$

10 | 9

$9 - 5 = \underline{4}$

$10 + 4 = \underline{14}$

**h** $16 - 5 = \underline{11}$

10 | 6

$6 - 5 = \underline{1}$

$10 + 1 = \underline{11}$

**i** $17 - 5 = \underline{12}$

10 | 7

$7 - 5 = \underline{2}$

$10 + 2 = \underline{12}$

**c**

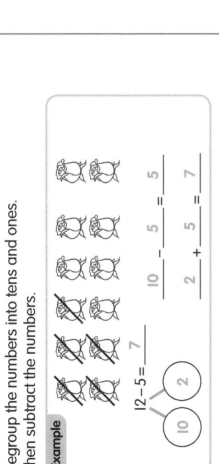

17 − 8 = 9

(circles: 7, 10)

10 − 8 = 2

7 + 2 = 9

**d**

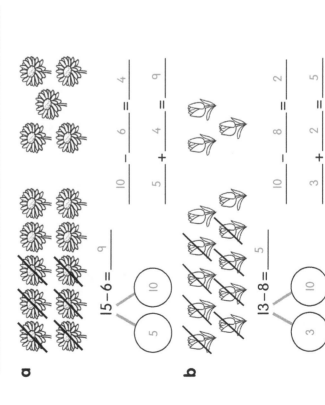

12 − 6 = 6

(circles: 2, 10)

10 − 6 = 4

2 + 4 = 6

**e**

18 − 9 = 9

(circles: 8, 10)

10 − 9 = 1

8 + 1 = 9

---

**3** Regroup the numbers into tens and ones. Then subtract the numbers.

**Example**

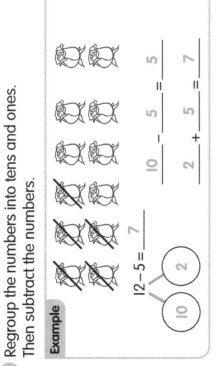

12 − 5 = 7

(circles: 10, 2)

10 − 5 = 5

2 + 5 = 7

**a**

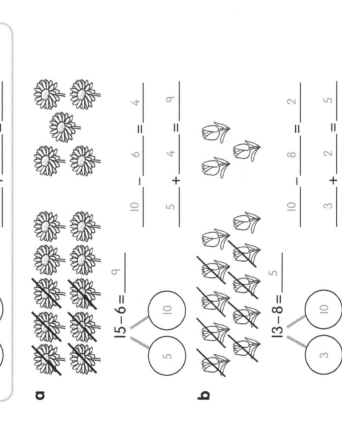

15 − 6 = 9

(circles: 5, 10)

10 − 6 = 4

5 + 4 = 9

**b**

13 − 8 = 5

(circles: 3, 10)

10 − 8 = 2

3 + 2 = 5

**4** Complete the subtraction sentences.

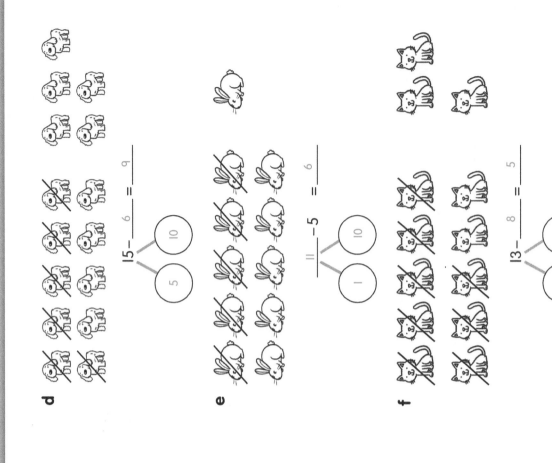

a   $16 - 7 = 9$

number bond: 10 and 6

b   $14 - 5 = 9$

number bond: 10 and 4

c   $12 - 7 = 5$

number bond: 10 and 2

d   $15 - 6 = 9$

number bond: 10 and 5

e   $11 - 5 = 6$

number bond: 10 and 1

f   $13 - 8 = 5$

number bond: 10 and 3

## Practice 4   Solving word problems

**1** Hardeep has 5 small toy cars.
He has 7 big toy cars.
How many toy cars does he
have altogether?

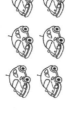
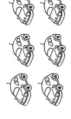

$5 + 7 = 12$

Hardeep has ___12___ toy cars altogether.

**2** Omar has 8 marbles.
Miya gives him 9 marbles.
How many marbles does Omar
have now?

$8 + 9 = 17$

Omar has ___17___ marbles now.

**3** Ruby has 13 pencils.
She gives 5 pencils to Peter.
How many pencils does
Ruby have left?

$13 - 5 = 8$

Ruby has ___8___ pencils left.

---

**5** Subtract the numbers.

**a** $16 - 6 =$ ___10___    **b** $12 - 4 =$ ___8___

**c** $14 - 6 =$ ___8___    **d** $15 - 9 =$ ___6___

**e** $13 - 8 =$ ___5___    **f** $17 - 8 =$ ___9___

**6** Which number fell into the number machine?
Write the number in ◯.

In

Subtract 9

Out

17

8

Date: _____

## Challenging Practice

**1** Write + or – in each circle.

a  10 ⊖ 6 = 4

b  7 ⊕ 5 = 12

c  16 ⊖ 9 = 7

d  9 ⊕ 7 = 16

e  11 ⊕ 3 = 14

f  14 ⊕ 6 = 20

g  17 ⊖ 2 = 15

h  12 ⊕ 8 = 20

**2** Fill in the spaces.

a  18 – __10__ = 8

b  __20__ – 10 = 10

c  20 – __0__ = 20

d  __15__ – 9 = 6

e  __9__ + 3 = 12

f  __8__ + 5 = 13

**4** Jack bakes 12 cakes.
He gives away some cakes.
He has 4 cakes left.
How many cakes does he
give away?

12 – 4 = 8

He gives away __8__ cakes.

**5** Millie makes some bracelets.
She gives 7 bracelets to
her friends.
She has 9 bracelets left.
How many bracelets did
Millie make?

7 + 9 = 16

Millie made __16__ bracelets.

## Problem Solving

1 The most star jumps that Peter and Ruby can do altogether is 20. Peter can do 6 more star jumps than Ruby. How many star jumps can Peter and Ruby each do?

Write down four possible pairs of numbers.

a If Ruby can do _____ star jumps, then Peter

can do _____ star jumps.

b If Ruby can do _____ star jumps, then Peter

can do _____ star jumps.

c If Peter can do _____ star jumps, then Ruby

can do _____ star jumps.

d If Peter can do _____ star jumps, then Ruby

can do _____ star jumps.

Answers vary. Examples:
a 1;7
b 7;13
c 8;12
d 12;6

---

3 Tai lands 2 aeroplanes in his favourite computer game.
His total score is 16.

a Colour 2 aeroplanes that he lands.

Answers vary

b Write an addition sentence for the aeroplanes you chose.

_____ + _____ = 16      Answers vary

c Look for other answers. Write them here.

_____ + _____ = 16

_____ + _____ = 16      Answers vary

**2** Fill the ◯ with these numbers.

| 2 | 3 | 5 | 6 |
|---|---|---|---|

The numbers in each line must add up to 12. For example, 1 + 4 + 7 = 12

Use each number once.

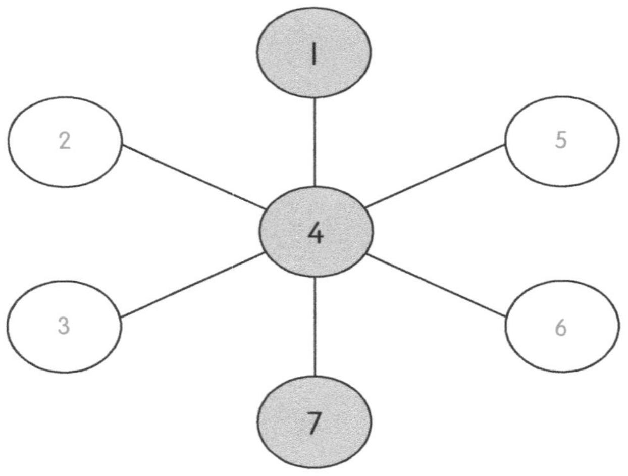

Unit 8: Addition and Subtraction within 20

# Unit 9: Length

| Week | Learning Objectives | Thinking Skills | Resources |
|---|---|---|---|
| 6 | **(1) Comparing two things**<br><br>Pupils will be able to compare the lengths of two objects using the terms 'tall/taller', 'long/longer', 'short/shorter' and 'high/higher'.<br><br>*Let's Explore!*<br>Pupils will be able to describe the relative height and length of two items. | • Comparing | • Pupil Textbook 1A, pp 110 to 113<br>• Practice Book 1B, pp 95 to 98<br>• Teacher's Guide 1A, pp 220 to 223 |
| 6 | **(2) Comparing more things**<br><br>Pupils will be able to compare the lengths of more than two objects using the terms 'tallest', 'longest', 'shortest' and 'highest'. | • Sequencing<br>• Comparing | • Pupil Textbook 1A, pp 114 to 116<br>• Practice Book 1B, pp 99 to 102<br>• Teacher's Guide 1A, pp 224 to 226 |

# Unit 9: Length

| Week | Learning Objectives | Thinking Skills | Resources |
|---|---|---|---|
| 6 | **(3) Using a start line**<br>Pupils will be able to use a common starting point when comparing lengths. | • Sequencing<br>• Comparing | • Pupil Textbook IA, pp 117 to 118<br>• Practice Book IB, pp 103 to 104<br>• Teacher's Guide IA, pp 227 to 228 |
| 7 | **(4) Measuring things**<br>Pupils will be able to measure lengths using objects as non-standard units. | • Sequencing<br>• Comparing | • Pupil Textbook IA, pp 119 to 122<br>• Practice Book IB, pp 105 to 108<br>• Teacher's Guide IA, pp 229 to 232 |
| 7 | **(5) Finding length in units**<br>Pupils will be able to use the term 'unit' to describe length. | • Sequencing<br>• Comparing | • Pupil Textbook IA, pp 123 to 125<br>• Practice Book IB, pp 109 to 112<br>• Teacher's Guide IA, pp 233 to 235 |

# Medium-term plan

| Week | Learning Objectives | Thinking Skills | Resources |
|------|--------------------|-----------------|-----------|
| 7 | *Put On Your Thinking Caps!*<br>Pupils will be able to:<br>• discriminate the use of unit length to determine the length of objects<br>• use a grid to help them determine and compare lengths of objects | • Comparing<br>• Induction<br>• Deduction<br><br>Heuristic for problem solving:<br>• Using a diagram | • Pupil Textbook 1A, p 126<br>• Practice Book 1B, pp 113 to 116<br>• Teacher's Guide 1A, p 236 |
| | Revision 1 | | • Practice Book 1B, pp 117 to 120 |

## Summative assessment opportunities

Assessment Book 1, Test 4, pp 39 to 44
For extension, Assessment Book 1, Challenging Problems 2, pp 45 to 46
Assessment Book 1, Check-up 2, pp 47 to 58

# Length

## Learning objective: Comparing two things

**Pupils will be able to:**

- compare the lengths of two objects using the terms 'tall/taller', 'long/longer', 'short/shorter' and 'high/higher'

## Key concept

The lengths of two objects can be compared using the terms 'tall/taller', 'long/longer', 'short/shorter' and 'high/higher'.

## Teaching sequence

- Ask pupils what "tall", "short", "taller" and "shorter" mean. Summarise pupils' ideas and explanations about these words.
- Use the example in the textbook to explain the terms.
- Show pupils some objects from around the classroom. Use the terms 'tall/taller' and 'short/shorter'. Explain to pupils that we use these terms to compare the length of objects.

- Ask pupils to compare their heights with a partner.
- Encourage pupils to say:

  "_____ is *taller than* _____."

  "_____ is *shorter than* _____."

## What you will need

- Objects of different lengths, e.g., string, wool, strips of paper, etc.
- Pupils' stationery, e.g. rubbers, pencils, pencil case etc.
- Blank paper

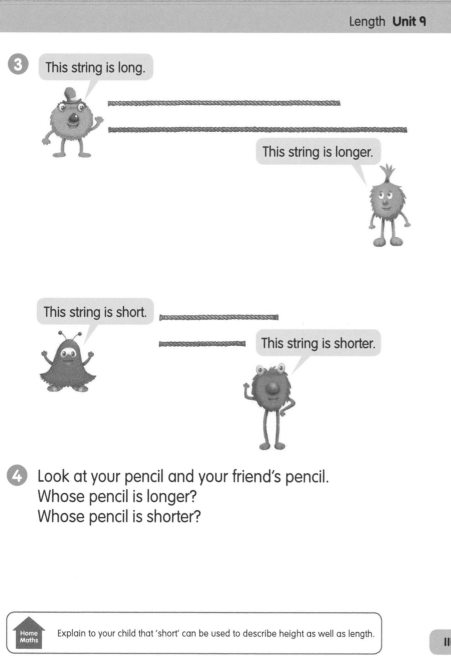

3  This string is long.

This string is longer.

This string is short.

This string is shorter.

4  Look at your pencil and your friend's pencil.
Whose pencil is longer?
Whose pencil is shorter?

III

## Teaching sequence

- Show pupils a piece of string. Attach it to the board. Ask pupils how long a string would be if it was longer than the string you have put on the board.
- Ask pupils to draw a longer 'string' next to the string on the board.
- Display a few more items and ask pupils to choose items that are longer than the string on the board. Encourage pupils to use sentences such as:
  *"The green string is longer than the white string."*
- Repeat this with a string that is shorter than the string on the board.
- Ask pupils to draw a line on a piece of paper and call it Line A. Ask them to draw lines that are longer than or shorter than Line A and label the lines. Encourage pupils to use sentences such as:
  *"Line A is shorter than Line B."*

4

- Ask pupils to compare the lengths of their rubbers, pencils etc. with their friends'.
- Ask pupils to draw the items on a piece of paper and write sentences below using the terms 'longer' or 'shorter'.

**Unit 9:** Length   **221**

## Thinking skill

Comparing

## What you will need

- Objects placed at different heights
- 10 cubes for each group

## Additional activity

Ask pupils to work in groups. Give each group some cubes. Ask one pupil to think of a number. Ask the groups to use this number to make a train or tower. Next ask the groups to make a train that is longer. Then ask the groups to make a tower that is taller.

## Note

'Higher' refers to the position of the object relative to the position of another object from the ground, whereas 'longer', 'shorter' and 'taller' compares the absolute lengths of two objects.

## Teaching sequence

- Place two objects at different heights. Ask pupils to identify the higher object using the term 'higher'.
- Repeat using other objects at different heights.
- Ask pupils to look at the picture in the textbook. Ask: "*Who is higher, Farha or Jack?*"
- Encourage pupils to say: "*Farha is higher than Jack.*"

**6**

- Ask pupils to raise their hands. Ask them if they can raise their hands higher.
- Invite volunteers to place items at different heights in the classroom and make sentences using 'higher'.
- Emphasise that when comparing two things, the terms 'taller', 'shorter', 'longer' and 'higher' are used.

**7**

**a**

- Ask pupils to work in groups. Ask each group to make a 3-cube tower. Ask pupils to make towers that are taller and shorter than the 3-cube tower.

**b**

- Ask each group to make a 5-cube train. Ask pupils to make trains that are longer and shorter than the 5-cube train.

Unit 9 Length

**5**

I am higher.

I am high.

**6** Raise your hand.
Now raise it higher.

### Activity

**7** **a** Make a tower with 3 .
Name it Tower A.
Make a tower taller than Tower A.
Make a tower shorter than Tower A.

Tower A

**b** Make a number train with 5 .
Name it Train X.
Make a train longer than Train X.
Make a train shorter than Train X.

Train X

Ask your child to look at things around the house and to compare their heights and lengths. Ask them to say which is taller/longer/shorter/higher. For example, "The stool is shorter than the table." "The tablespoon is longer than the teaspoon."

112

Practice Book 1B, p.95

## Objective of activity

Pupils will be able to describe the relative height and length of two items.

## Independent work

Practice 1 in Practice Book 1B, pp 95 to 98.

## Teaching sequence

**8** *Let's Explore!*

- Ask pupils to work in groups.
- Encourage pupils to make up stories about the lengths and heights of the various objects in the picture using the helping words given.

**Example:**

*"Ruby and Millie are gardening. There are two sunflowers. One is taller than the other. There are two worms. One is shorter than the other."*

## Let's Explore!

**8**

Ruby and Millie are gardening.
Talk about this picture with a partner.
Use these words.

| | |
|---|---|
| tall | taller |
| long | longer |
| high | higher |
| short | shorter |

113

## Learning objective: Comparing more things

**Pupils will be able to:**

- compare the lengths of more than two objects using the terms 'tallest', 'longest', 'shortest' and 'highest'

## What you will need

- 3 objects of different lengths
- 3 objects at different heights
- Bookshelf with items on different shelves

## Key concept

The lengths of more than two objects can be compared using the terms 'tallest', 'longest', 'shortest' and 'highest'.

## Teaching sequence

- Write the terms 'tallest', 'longest', 'shortest' and 'highest' on the board. Ask pupils what they think these words mean.
- Emphasise that when the length of more than two things are compared, the terms 'tallest', 'longest', 'shortest' and 'highest' are used.
- Look at the picture and point out who is tallest (Tom) and who is shortest (Miya).
- Display three different objects and compare their heights. Teach pupils to use the terms 'tallest' and 'shortest'. E.g. "*The red box is the tallest.*"
- Ask pupils to compare the lengths of the umbrellas in the picture. E.g. "*Miya has the longest umbrella and Ethan has the shortest umbrella.*"
- Show three different objects and compare their lengths. Encourage pupils to use the terms 'longest' and 'shortest'. E.g. "*The green string is the longest.*"
- Compare the positions of the shoes on the shelf. E.g. "*The wellington boots are on the highest shelf.*"
- Display items on the bookshelf and compare their positions. Teach pupils to use the term 'highest'. E.g. "*The pencils are on the highest shelf.*"

---

**Unit 9** Length

**Let's Learn!**

**Comparing more things**

Miya          Ethan          Tom

Miya is the **shortest**.

Tom is the **tallest**.

Miya has the **longest** umbrella.

Ethan has the **shortest** umbrella.

The wellington boots are on the **highest** shelf.

114

## Additional activity

Give pupils three different coloured strips of paper but of the same length.

Ask pupils to cut off part of each paper strip so that the remaining strips are of different lengths.

Ask pupils to arrange their remaining strips in order, and to write sentences to describe them.

E.g.

1) The yellow strip is the shortest.
2) The blue strip is longer than the red strip.

### 2

Look at the animals.

> Which is the tallest animal? giraffe
>
> Which is the shortest animal? meerkat
>
> Which animal is longer, the crocodile or the snake?
> crocodile
>
> Which animal is taller than the ostrich? giraffe
>
> Which animal is shorter than the zebra? lion/meerkat

115

## Teaching sequence

### 2

Look for pupils who can use the terms appropriately to answer questions about the picture.

## Thinking skills
- Sequencing
- Comparing

## What you will need
30 cubes for each group

## Independent work
Practice 2 and *Maths Journal* and Practice 2 in Practice Book 1B, pp 99 to 102.

## Additional activity
Show the picture in Practice Book 1B, p 102, to pupils. Consolidate pupils' learning by asking them to say or write sentences about the picture using the terms 'taller', 'longer', 'shorter', 'higher', 'tallest', 'longest', 'shortest' and 'highest'.

## Teaching sequence

**a**
- Ask pupils to work in groups to make the 2-cube, 3-cube, 4-cube and 5-cube towers in the textbook.
- Ask pupils to make a tower taller than the tallest tower and another tower shorter than the shortest tower.
- Ask pupils to arrange their towers in ascending or descending order of height and write down sentences such as 'The blue tower is the tallest.' and 'The yellow tower is the shortest.'
- Incorporate 'taller' and 'shorter' into this activity. Encourage pupils to describe their towers. E.g. "The blue tower is taller than the red tower."

**b**
- Ask each group to find the longest, tallest and shortest things, including people in the classroom.

**c**
- Ask pupils to identify the longest word.

---

**Unit 9** Length

### Activity

**3 a** Make four towers.
Place them in order.

You can start with the tallest or the shortest tower.

Make a tower taller than the tallest tower.

Make a tower shorter than the shortest tower.

**b** Find these in your classroom:
1. the longest object
2. the tallest object
3. the shortest object

**c** Which is the longest word?

A c h e r r y i s r e d .

cherry

Practice Book 1B, p.99

116

## Learning objective:
## Using a start line

**Pupils will be able to:**

- use a common starting point when comparing lengths

## Key concept

A common starting point makes comparison of lengths easier.

## What you will need

5 fish cut from photocopy master 18 (see page 272)

## Additional activity

Show pupils five straws of different lengths, without aligning them. Label them A to E. Alternatively, you could put magnetic strips of different lengths on the board. Invite a volunteer to guess which is the longest straw without them touching or aligning the straws. Ask them what would help them to compare the straws.

---

## Let's Learn!

### Using a start line

**1**

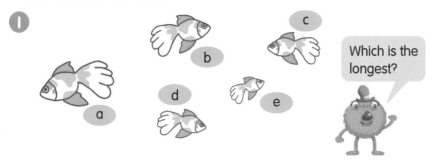

c

b

Which is the longest?

d

e

a

Putting objects along a start line helps you to see which is the longest.

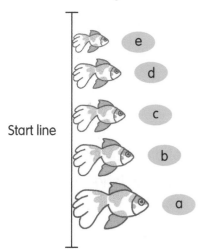

e

d

c

Start line

b

a

Which fish is the longest? a

117

## Teaching sequence

**1**

- Label the fish cut from the Photocopy master A, B, C, D and E. Arrange them randomly on the board. (Some of the fish should be almost equal in length so that from a distance, they may look the same.)

- Ask pupils to tell you the sequence of the fish in terms of their length. Discuss pupils' answers.

- Draw a line on the board and place the fish along the line, but not in order. Now ask pupils to sequence the fish in terms of their length again. Ask them if it is now easier to compare their lengths.

- Ask pupils to look at the fish and the start line in the textbook. Explain to them that the start line helps us to compare the lengths of the fish.

## Thinking skills
- Sequencing
- Comparing

## What you will need
- Traced copies or photocopies of the strips on the page (see Photocopy master 19 on page 273)
- A4 paper and glue for each pair of pupils

## Independent work
Practice 3 in Practice Book 1B, pp 103 to 104.

## Teaching sequence

- Ask pupils which is the longest/shortest strip. Ask them what would help them to compare the strips.
- Trace and cut out the strips and place them along a start line and ask pupils to compare the lengths.

- Ask pupils to work in pairs and give them paper to cut out three strips of different lengths.
- Ask pupils to find the longest and shortest strips by drawing a start line and aligning the rectangular strips with it. Ask pupils to share the strips with the class.
- Increase the level of difficulty by asking pupils to cut out more rectangular strips of different lengths.

2 Look at the strips of paper.
   a Which is the longest? A
   b Which is the shortest? F

What can you use to help you? A start line.

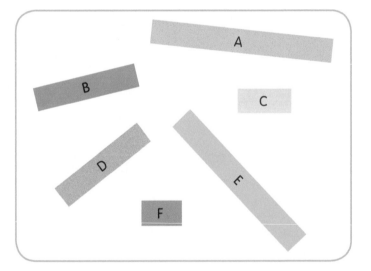

## Activity

3 Cut three strips of paper of different lengths.

Ask a partner to say which is the longest and which is the shortest.

Practice Book 1B, p.103

118

## Learning objective:
## Measuring things

**Pupils will be able to:**

- measure lengths using objects as non-standard units

## What you will need

- Long straws (of uniform length) for each group
- Paper clips (of uniform length) for each group

## Key concept

Length can be measured using objects as non-standard units.

## Thinking skills

- Sequencing
- Comparing

---

# Let's Learn!

## Measuring things

1 Look at the picture.

Make sure all the paper clips are the same length.

The book is **about** 5 paper clips long.
We can also say that its length is about 5 paper clips.

## Activity

2 Use drinking straws to measure the following:

a the teacher's table
b your table
c your book

Which is the longest?
Which is the shortest?
Is your table longer than the teacher's table?

  **Home Maths** Explain to your child that we say 'about' when a measurement is not exact.

---

## Teaching sequence

**1**

- Explain to pupils that we can measure length using objects, such as paper clips and straws, provided that the objects are all of the same length and that we have enough of them.
- Ask pupils to look at the book in the picture. Paper clips are placed next to the book one after another. Ask pupils to count the number of paper clips. Explain to them that the length of the book is about 5 paper clips long.
- Ask pupils why we use 'about'.

**2**

- Ask pupils to guess the number of straws needed to measure the length of the board. Fix the straws end-to-end against the board and count them. To emphasise that the measurement is approximate, use the phrase "*about __ straws*". Explain to pupils that it is important for the first straw to be placed at the edge and that the straws must not overlap.
- Ask pupils to work in groups. Ask each group to guess the length of your table, their own tables and a book using straws or paper clips. Next ask them to measure the lengths using straws or paper clips.
- Ask pupils to complete the questions.

## Additional activity

Ask pupils to measure some objects, e.g. their table, using two different non-standard units of measurement, such as straws, paper clips or pencils. Point out that the measurements are different, although the lengths of the objects are unchanged. Explain that this is due to the smaller/bigger units of measurement used (i.e. straws are longer than paper clips, so fewer straws are needed to measure the table).

## Teaching sequence

- Look for pupils who can make reasonable estimates and count the units accurately.
- Ask pupils to describe the lengths of the objects.

③ Look at the pictures.

pencil

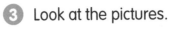

pencil case

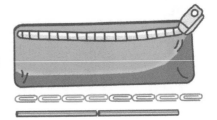

water bottle

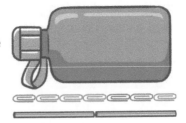

**a** How long is the pencil? about 5 paper clips long

**b** How long is the pencil case? about 8 paper clips long

**c** How long is the water bottle? about 7 paper clips long
about 2 drinking straws long

**d** Which is the longest? pencil case

**e** Is the pencil longer than the pencil case? No

120

Length **Unit 9**

## Activity

4  Work with a partner.

I  Cut a strip of paper like the one below.

2  Make 4 more strips of the same length.

3  Ask your partner to use these strips to measure the length of your arm.

4  Trace round your foot on a piece of paper.

5  Use the strips of paper to measure the length of your foot.

My arm is about ⬚ strips of paper long.
Answers vary

My foot is about ⬚ strips of paper long.
Answers vary

I2I

## Teaching sequence

④

- Ask pupils to trace and cut out the strip in the textbook or use the Photocopy master.
- Guide pupils to follow the instructions to measure the length of their arms and feet.

## Thinking skills

- Sequencing
- Comparing

## What you will need

- Strips of the same and different lengths, labelled A, B, C, etc. for each group. Make the strips for each group the same.
- Paper clips for each group

## Independent work

Practice 4 in Practice Book 1B, pp 105 to 108. Give pupils ten paper clips and ten 20p coins for question (1) and some lolly sticks for question (3).

## Teaching sequence

- Ask pupils to work in groups. Give strips of the same and different lengths, and one paper clip to each group.
- Ask one pupil from each group to hold up paper strip A and one paper clip. Ask the group to guess the length of the strip in terms of the number of paper clips. Ask one pupil in each group to record the guesses in a table.
- Ask pupils to repeat the activity for the other strips.
- After the groups have completed their guesses, give out more paper clips to each group. Ask the groups to measure the strips and record their answers.
- Ask pupils to complete the activity and discuss their answers.

### Activity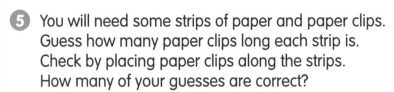

⑤ You will need some strips of paper and paper clips. Guess how many paper clips long each strip is. Check by placing paper clips along the strips. How many of your guesses are correct?

Which strips have the same length?
Which is the longest strip?
Which is the shortest strip?

Put the strips in order from the longest to the shortest.

Practice Book 1B, p.105

122

## Learning objective:
## Finding length in units

**Pupils will be able to:**

- use the term 'unit' to describe length

## Key concept

Length can be described using the term 'unit' instead of paper clips or lolly sticks.

---

## Let's Learn!

**Finding length in units**

  stands for 1 unit.

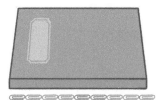

The loaf of bread is about 7 units long.

**2** ⊂▭⊃ stands for 1 unit.

How many units long is this book? About 9 units long

123

---

## Teaching sequence

- Ask pupils to look at the picture in the textbook. Ask pupils how long the bread is in terms of the number of lolly sticks. Encourage pupils to say: "*The loaf of bread is about 7 lolly sticks long.*"
- Explain to pupils that 'units' are used to describe the length of objects.
- Explain to pupils that 1 lolly stick represents 1 unit. Ask pupils to replace 'lolly sticks' with 'units' and read the sentence again.

- Encourage pupils to count the number of paper clips beside the book.
- Explain to pupils that 1 paper clip represents 1 unit. Ask pupils to give the length in terms of units. "*The book is about 9 units long.*"

## Teaching sequence

- Ask pupils to answer the questions. Look for pupils who can use the terms 'longer than' and 'shorter than' appropriately.

**3** It's bedtime for Jack.

Look at the things in the bathroom.

Each ☐ stands for I unit.

**a** How long is the towel rack? I unit long

**b** How tall is the shower curtain? 6 units tall

**c** Is the towel rack longer than the mirror?
No

**d** Which is shorter, the towel or the towel rack? towel rack

124

**234** Unit 9: Length

## Thinking skills

- Sequencing
- Comparing

## What you will need

- Lolly sticks and paper clips for each group
- Book for each group
- Pencil for each group

## Independent work

Practice 5 in Practice Book 1B, pp 109 to 112.

 Activity

④ Use  to measure the objects shown.

Then use ╱ to measure.

Copy the chart. Fill in your answers.

| | Number of 📎 | Number of ╱ |
|---|---|---|
| Table | | |
| Book | | |
| Pencil | | |

Practice Book 1B, p.109

## Teaching sequence

④

- Ask pupils to work in groups. Ask them to measure the objects (table, book and pencil) with lolly sticks and paper clips and to say the lengths in units.
- Ask each group to share their answers with the class.

Home Maths — Explain to your child that using different objects to stand for 1 unit gives different measurements. Remind your child that we use the same object to compare the lengths of 2 different items.

125

## Objectives of activity

**Pupils will be able to:**

- discriminate the use of unit length to determine the length of objects
- use a grid to help them determine and compare lengths of objects

## Teaching sequence

**5** *Put On Your Thinking Caps!*

**a**

- Ask pupils to look at the picture in the textbook, then answer the question. Look for pupils who notice that the bread is about 8 lolly sticks long, and the book is about 9 paper clips long.
- Explain that we can't say that the book is longer than the loaf of bread because we don't know the length of each lolly stick and paper clip.
- Explain that as the lolly stick is longer than the paper clip, the bread may be longer than the book although the number of lolly sticks used is fewer than the number of paper clips used.
- Explain that we can't compare lengths of objects using different non-standard units.

**b**

- Ask pupils to look at the two pictures, then answer the question.
- Explain to pupils: Set 1 has spaces between horizontal lines that can represent non-standard units. However because the leaves are aligned horizontally, the spaces cannot be used as units for measurement.
- Explain to pupils: Set 2 has spaces marked out by vertical lines that represent non-standard units. As the leaves are aligned horizontally, the spaces can be used as units for measurement. Leaves A and B are both about 1 unit long and leaf C is about 3 units long.

## Thinking skills

- Comparing
- Induction
- Deduction

## Heuristics for problem solving

Using a diagram

## Independent work

*Challenging Practice, Problem Solving* and Revision I in Practice Book IB, pp 113 to 120.

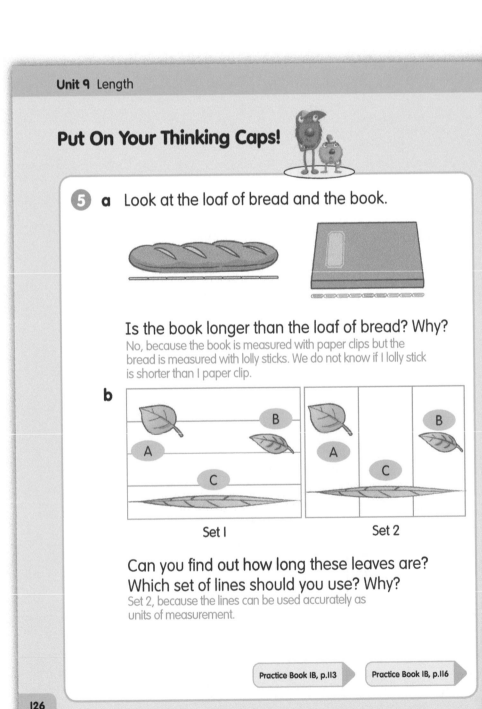

## Put On Your Thinking Caps!

**5** **a** Look at the loaf of bread and the book.

Is the book longer than the loaf of bread? Why?

No, because the book is measured with paper clips but the bread is measured with lolly sticks. We do not know if 1 lolly stick is shorter than 1 paper clip.

**b**

Set I                    Set 2

Can you find out how long these leaves are? Which set of lines should you use? Why?

Set 2, because the lines can be used accurately as units of measurement.

Practice Book IB, p.113          Practice Book IB, p.116

126

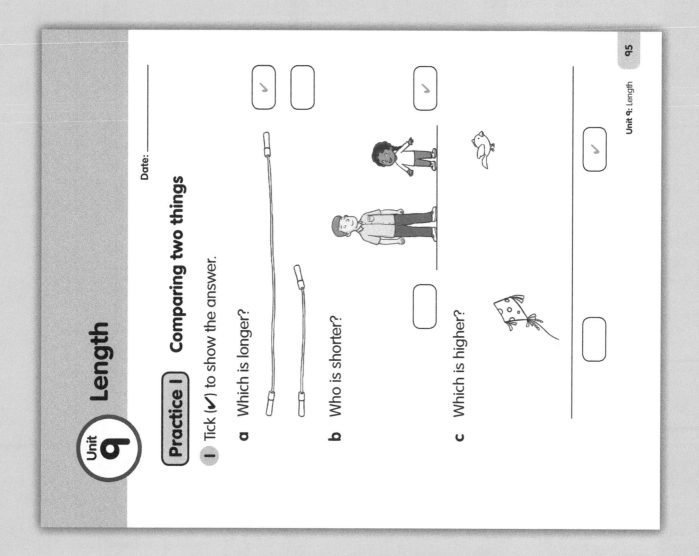

# Unit 9 Length

Date: _____

**Practice 1** | **Comparing two things**

1 Tick (✔) to show the answer.

**a** Which is longer?

**b** Who is shorter?

**c** Which is higher?

**b** Which is higher?

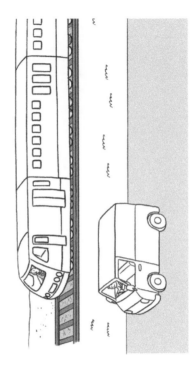

The clouds are ___higher___ than the aeroplane.

**c** Which is longer?
Which is shorter?

The train is ___longer___ than the van.

The van is ___shorter___ than the train.

---

**2** Fill in the spaces.

**Example**

Which is longer?
Which is shorter?

snake

caterpillar

The snake is ___longer___ than the caterpillar.

The caterpillar is ___shorter___ than the snake.

**a** Which is shorter?
Which is taller?

The tree is ___taller___ than the giraffe.

The giraffe is ___shorter___ than the tree.

## Practice 2 Comparing more things

**1** Colour:

**Example**

the longest string of beads

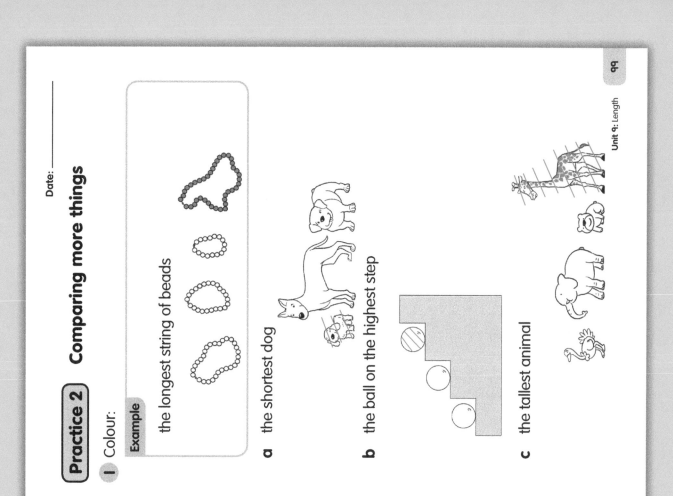

**a** the shortest dog

**b** the ball on the highest step

**c** the tallest animal

---

**3** Draw:

**Example**

a longer arrow

**a** a shorter tree

*Answers vary*

**b** a ball on a higher shelf

*Answers vary*

**c** a longer and taller ship

*Answers vary*

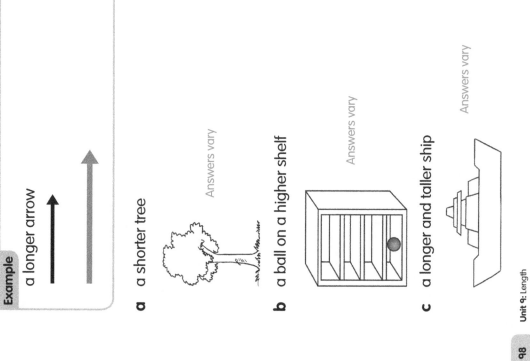

4 Look at the pictures.

a Who has the tallest beanstalks?

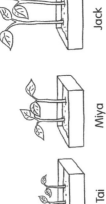

Tai          Miya          Jack

_Jack_ has the tallest beanstalks.

b Which string is the longest?

very curly string

curly string

straight string

The _very curly_ string is the longest.

---

2 Fill in the spaces with **taller, tallest, shorter** or **shortest.**

A          B          C

a Tree B is the _tallest_ tree.

b The giraffe is _taller_ than Tree A.

c The _shortest_ tree is Tree C.

d Tree B is _taller_ than Tree A.

e Tree C is _shorter_ than the giraffe.

3 Fill in the spaces with **higher** or **highest.**

Farha          Peter          Ella

a Farha is sitting on the _highest_ seat.

b Ella's seat is _higher_ than Peter's seat.

c Farha's seat is _higher_ than Ella's seat.

## Practice 3  Using a start line

1 Copy the caterpillars below.
Put them in the box in the order shown.

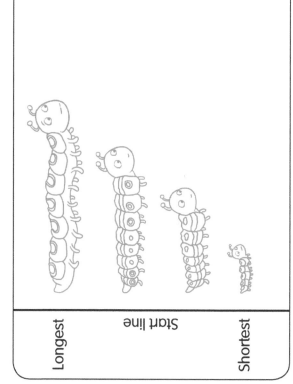

Longest

Start line

Shortest

---

## Maths Journal

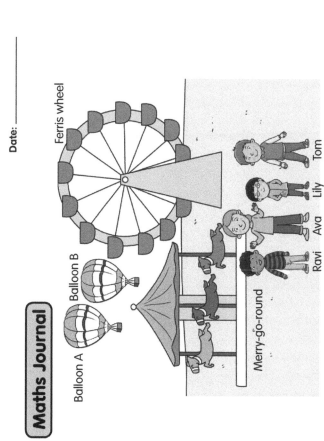

Balloon A  Balloon B  Ferris wheel  Merry-go-round  Ravi  Ava  Lily  Tom

Ravi, Ava, Lily and Tom are at the fairground.
Write five sentences using the words.

| taller | longer | shorter | higher |
| tallest | longest | shortest | highest |

Answers vary. Examples:

1 **Ava is the tallest girl.**

2 Balloon A is higher than balloon B.

3 Merry-go-round is shorter than Ferris wheel.

4 Ferris wheel is higher than balloon B.

5 Tom is taller than Lily.

6 The base of the Merry-go-round is longer than the base of the Ferris wheel.

## Practice 4 Measuring things

1 What is the length of each tape?
Use  and (20p) to find out.
Fill in the spaces.

**Example**

The tape is about __3__ paper clips long.

It is about __5__ coins long.

**a**

The tape is about _____ paper clips long.

It is about _____ coins long. Answers vary

**b**

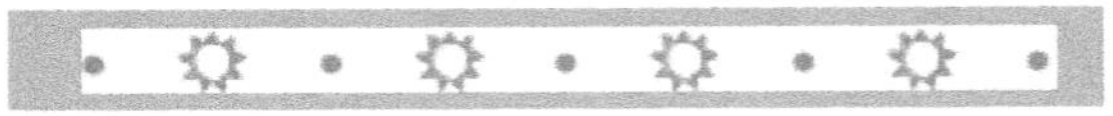

The tape is about _____ paper clips long.

It is about _____ coins long. Answers vary

2 Draw 2 more pencils.
Colour the longest pencil blue.
Colour the shortest pencil green.

**Start line**

Answers vary

**c**

The book is about __5__ long.

**d**

One side of the photo frame is about __6__ long.

**e**

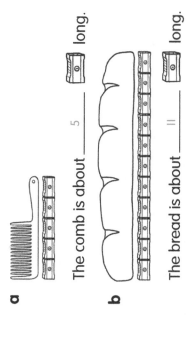

One side of the envelope is about __7__ long.

**c**

The tape is about ____ paper clips long.

It is about ____ coins long. *Answers vary*

**d**

The tape is about ____ paper clips long.

It is about ____ coins long. *Answers vary*

**2** Count and fill in the spaces.

**Example**

The pen is about __6__ long.

**a**

The comb is about __5__ long.

**b**

The bread is about __11__ long.

## Practice 5  Finding length in units

1 Fill in the spaces.

**Example**

▨ stands for 1 unit.

The spoon is about
**4** _____ units long.

**a**

▨ stands for 1 unit.

The book is about
6 _____ units long.

**b**

▨ stands for 1 unit.

The bat is about _____ 12 units long.

**c**

○ stands for 1 unit.

String A is about _____ 12 units long.

String B is about _____ 9 units long.

String A _____ is longer.

---

3 Look for these objects in your classroom.
Guess how long each object is.
Then measure the objects.

Use lolly sticks.

| Object | I Guess | I Measure |
|---|---|---|
| | About _____ lolly sticks _Answers vary_ | About _____ lolly sticks _Answers vary_ |
| | About _____ lolly sticks _Answers vary_ | About _____ lolly sticks _Answers vary_ |
| | About _____ lolly sticks _Answers vary_ | About _____ lolly sticks _Answers vary_ |

**a** Which is the longest , , or ?
_Answers vary_

**b** Which is longer or ?
_Answers vary_

**2** Look at the picture.
Fill in the spaces.

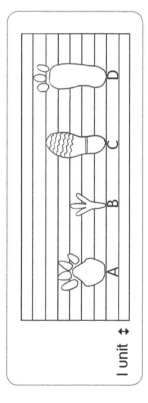

1 unit ↕

**a** Footprint A is ___4___ units long.

**b** Footprint B is ___3___ units long.

**c** Footprint C is ___5___ units long.

**d** Footprint D is ___6___ units long.

**e** Footprint ___D___ is the longest.

**f** Footprint ___B___ is shorter than Footprint A.

**3** ⬜ stands for 1 unit.

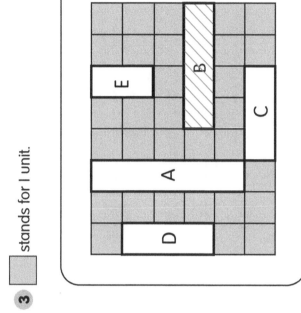

Fill in the spaces.

**a** Strip ___A___ is the longest.
It is ___5___ units long.

**b** Strip ___E___ is the shortest.
It is ___2___ units long.

**c** Strip ___C___ is as long as Strip ___D___.

**d** Colour the strip that is 4 units long.

## Challenging Practice

1 Millie moves the counters on a grid.
The arrows show her moves.

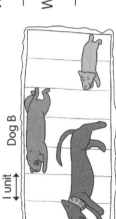

a Which counter makes the longest move? C

b Which counter makes the shortest move? B

c Which counter moves 5 squares? C

d Which counters move the same length? D and E.

2 Three dogs are lying on a rug.

Which is the longest dog? Dog A

Which is the shortest dog? Dog C

---

4 ☐ stands for 1 unit.

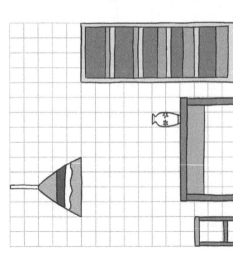

| |
|---|
| short |
| shorter |
| shortest |
| taller |
| tallest |
| longer |
| longest |
| higher |

Fill in the spaces.
Use the words above to help you.

a The table is _7_ units long.

b The bookshelf is _11_ units tall.

c Look at the stool, the table and the bookshelf.

The bookshelf is the _tallest_ thing.

The stool is _shorter_ than the table.

d The vase is the _shortest_ thing in the room.

**5**

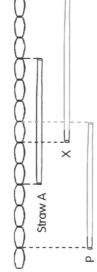

A    B    C    D

Arrange the animals in order.
Begin with the tallest.
Write the letters.

_____ _____ _____ _____
tallest

---

**3** Sue is taller than Bella.
Ann is the tallest.
Write the names of the children in the boxes.

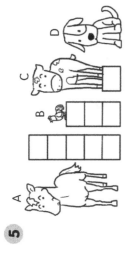

Ann        Sue        Bella

**4** ⬭ stands for 1 unit.

Straw A

P

X

**a** Draw a straw as long as Straw A.
Start at P.

**b** Draw a straw longer than Straw A.
Start at X.

# Revision I

1 Colour the star that makes 10.

   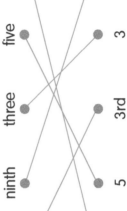

5 + 3    6 + 4    7 + 2    1 + 8

2 Circle the sixth loaf from the left.

3 Match.

third    ninth    three    five    nine

9    5    3rd    3    9th

---

## Problem Solving

1 Hardeep, Omar, Ella and Miya cut strips of paper.
Who does each strip belong to?

Omar's strip is longer than Miya's strip.

Ella's strip is the longest.

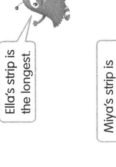

Miya's strip is longer than Hardeep's strip.

Fill in the spaces.

Strip A    _Ella_

Strip B    _Omar_

Strip C    _Miya_

Strip D    _Hardeep_

**4** Which one gives an answer greater than 5?
Cross (✗) it out.

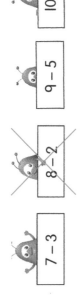

| 7 − 3 | 8 − 2 | 9 − 5 | 10 − 6 |

**5** Complete the number patterns.

a 1, 4, 7, __10__, ___, 13

b 20, ___, 18, ___, 16, 14, 12

**6** Complete the pattern.

**7** Match the number sentences that give the same answer.

| 1 + 7 = | 8 |
| 18 − 3 = | 15 |
| 14 + 6 = | 20 |
| 19 − 3 = | 16 |
| 15 − 6 = | 9 |

| 7 + 8 = | 15 |
| 2 + 7 = | 9 |
| 11 − 3 = | 8 |
| 20 − 0 = | 20 |
| 9 + 7 = | 16 |

1 + 7 = 8
11 − 3 = 8
They both give the same answer!

**8** Compare Set A and Set B.
Fill in the spaces.

Set A

Set B

Set __B__ has 4 more apples than Set __A__.

Set __A__ has 4 fewer apples than Set __B__.

**9** Fill in the spaces.

a 3 more than 4 is __7__.

b 5 less than 20 is __15__.

c __18__ is 2 more than 16.

d __5__ is 6 less than 11.

**10** Omar keeps his toys in a box.
He has 7 teddy bears.
He has 4 more aeroplanes than teddy bears.
He has 2 fewer cars than aeroplanes.
Write the number of each toy Omar has in his toy box.

Omar's toy box

| teddy bears | 7 | aeroplanes | 11 |
| cars | 9 | | |

**11** How long is each object?
Fill in the spaces.

**a** The pencil is about __4__ 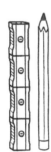 long.

**b** The chalk is about __2__  long.

**c** The pencil case is about __3__ ⎯ long.

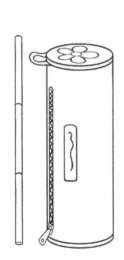

It is about __6__ 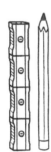 long.

**d** Which is the longest object? ___pencil case___

**e** Which is the shortest object? ___chalk___

# PHOTOCOPY MASTERS

Noogol

Googol

Koogol

Ooogol

Toogol

Zoogol

# Unit 1: Numbers to 10

Game (Pupil Textbook 1A, p 12)

Hit 10!

| Player \ Round | 1 | 2 | 3 | 4 | 5 | 6 | 7 | 8 | 9 | 10 |
|---|---|---|---|---|---|---|---|---|---|---|
| 1 | | | | | | | | | | |
| 2 | | | | | | | | | | |
| 3 | | | | | | | | | | |

# Unit I: Numbers to 10

## Put On Your Thinking Caps! (Pupil Textbook IA, p 2I)

| Numbers smaller than 5 | Numbers from 5 to 7 | Numbers greater than 7 |
|---|---|---|
| | | |

# Unit 2: Number Bonds

Activity (Pupil Textbook IA, p 23)

Number bonds that make _____

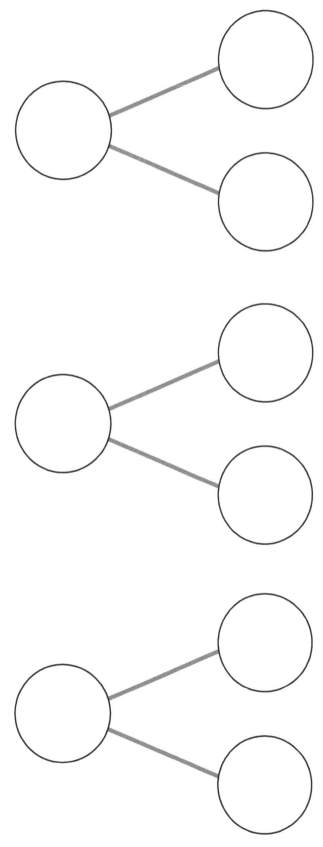

# Unit 2: Number Bonds

## Activity (Pupil Textbook IA, p 23)

Number bonds that make _____

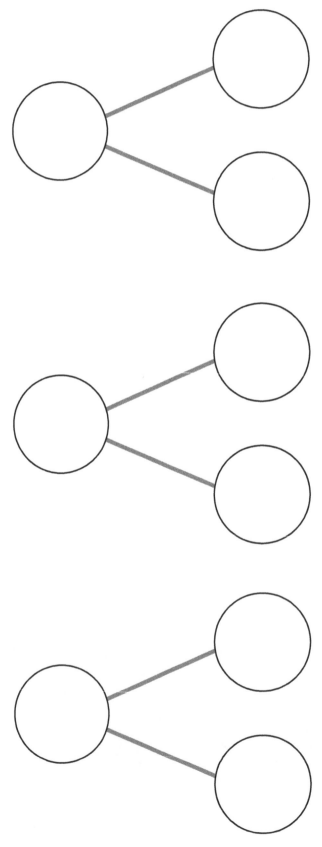

# Unit 2: Number Bonds

Let's Explore! (Pupil Textbook IA, p 25)

Number bonds that make _____

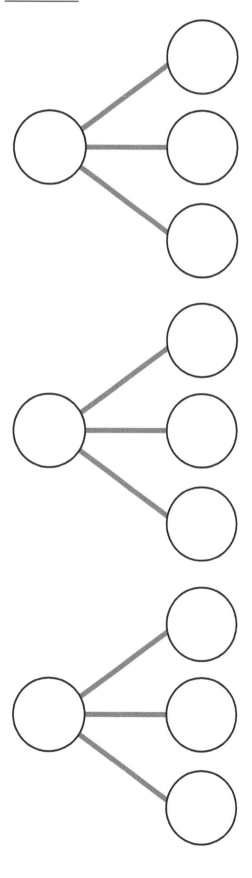

# Unit 2: Number Bonds

## Let's Explore! (Pupil Textbook IA, p 25)

Number bonds that make _____

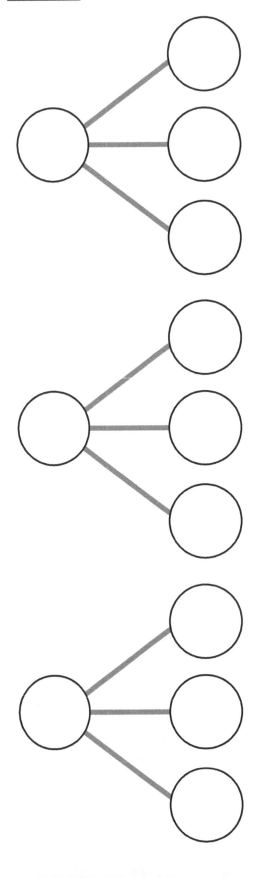

# Unit 3: Addition within 10

Activity (Pupil Textbook IA, p 29)

Start counting
from here

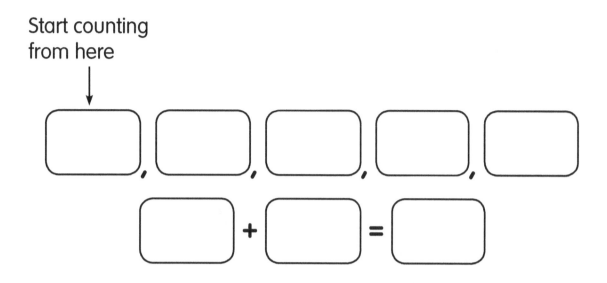

Start counting
from here

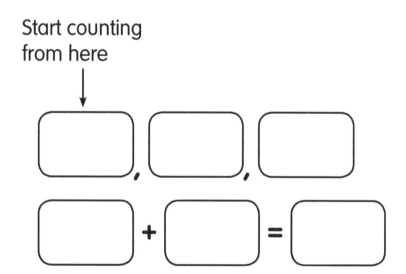

# Unit 3: Addition within 10

Game (Pupil Textbook IA, p 31)

## Card fun!

### Set A

| 1 | 2 | 3 | 0 |

| 1 | 2 | 3 |

### Set B

| 1 | 2 | 3 | 4 | 5 |

| 6 | 7 |

**Photocopy masters**

# Unit 3: Addition within 10

Put On Your Thinking Caps! (Pupil Textbook IA, p 38)

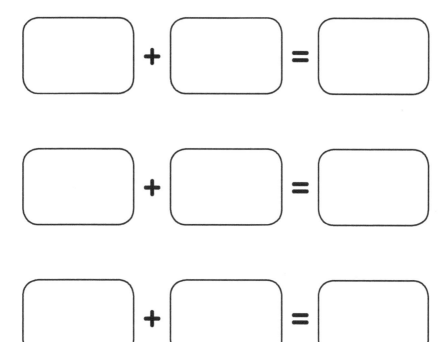

# Unit 4: Subtraction within 10

Let's Explore! (Pupil Textbook IA, p 52)

## Number sentence cards

| | | |
|---|---|---|
| 2 | 3 | 6 |
| 8 | 9 | 10 |
| + | − | = |

# Unit 4: Subtraction within 10

Put On Your Thinking Caps! (Pupil Textbook 1A, pp 52 to 53)

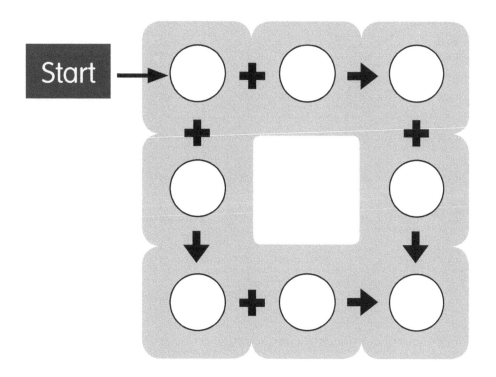

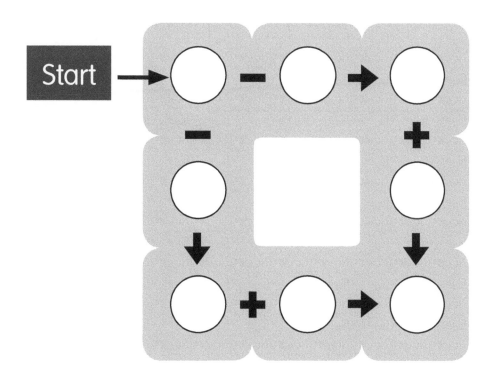

# Unit 5: Shapes and Patterns

Let's Learn! (Pupil Textbook IA, p 54)

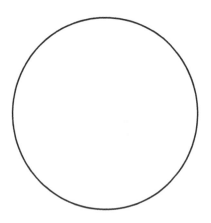

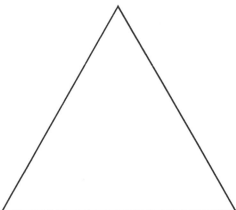

**Photocopy masters**

# Unit 5: Shapes and Patterns

Let's Learn! (Pupil Textbook IA, p 55)

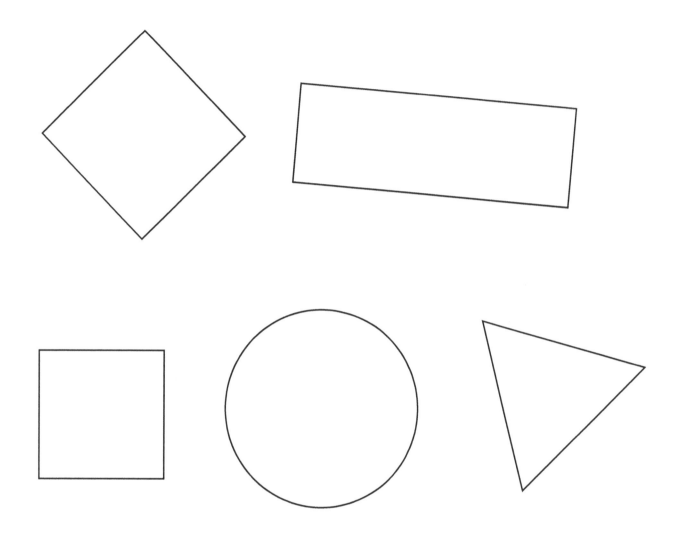

# Unit 5: Shapes and Patterns

Let's Explore! (Pupil Textbook IA, p 59)

## Unit 5: Shapes and Patterns

Let's Learn! (Pupil Textbook 1A, p 63)

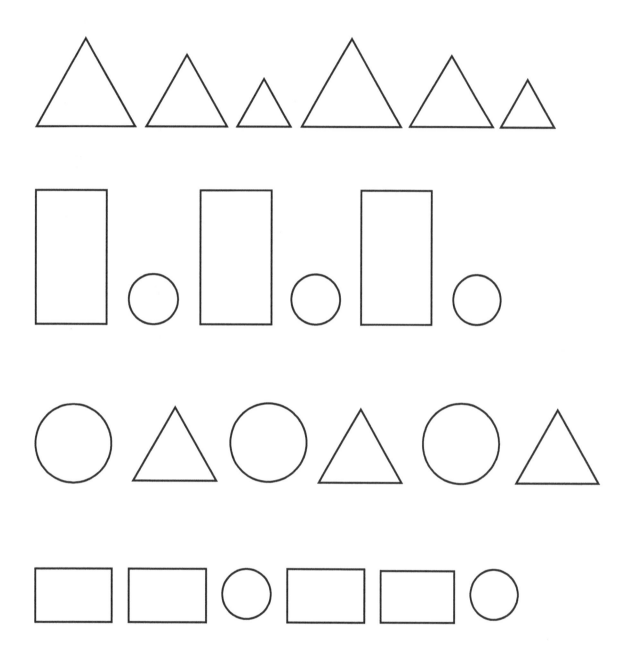

# Unit 6: Ordinal Numbers

Let's Explore! (Pupil Textbook 1A, p 76)

| No. | Position of red card from the left | Position of red card from the right | ( ) + ( ) |
|-----|-----|-----|-----|
| 1 | ( ) | ( ) | ( ) |
| 2 | ( ) | ( ) | ( ) |
| 3 | ( ) | ( ) | ( ) |
| 4 | ( ) | ( ) | ( ) |

# Unit 7: Numbers to 20

Put On Your Thinking Caps! (Pupil Textbook 1A, p 97)

| 10 | 14 | 16 | 20 |

| ? | ? |

| 12 | 14 | 15 | 16 |

| ? | ? |

# Unit 8: Addition and Subtraction within 20

Let's Explore! (Pupil Textbook IA, p 107)

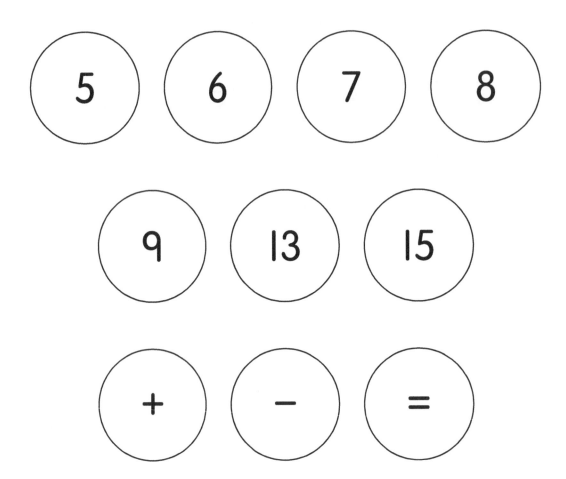

# Unit 8: Addition and Subtraction within 20

Put On Your Thinking Caps! (Pupil Textbook IA, pp 108 to 109)

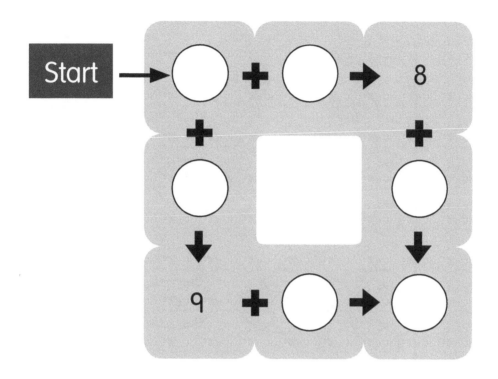

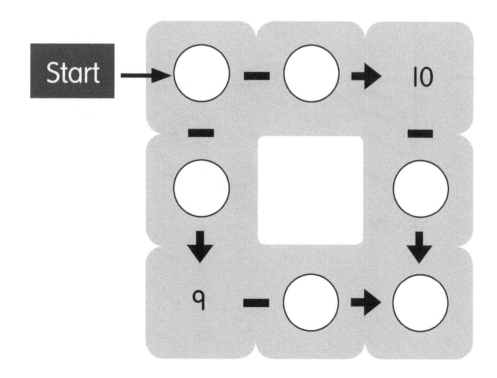

**Photocopy masters**

# Unit 9: Length

Let's Learn! (Pupil Textbook IA, p 117)

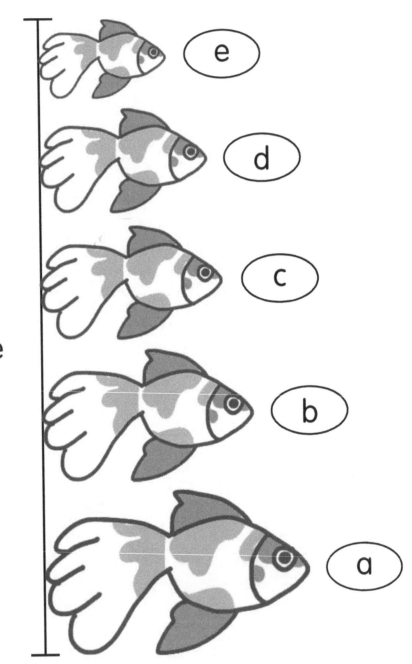

Start line

# Unit 9: Length

Let's Learn! (Pupil Textbook 1A, p 118)

| A |
|:---:|

| B |
|:---:|

| C |
|:---:|

| D |
|:---:|

| E |
|:---:|

| F |
|:---:|

# Unit 9: Length

Activity (Pupil Textbook 1A, p 121)

| | | | |
|---|---|---|---|
| | | | |

| | | | |
|---|---|---|---|
| | | | |

| | | | |
|---|---|---|---|
| | | | |

| | | | |
|---|---|---|---|
| | | | |

| | | | |
|---|---|---|---|
| | | | |